Prader-Willi Sydrome:
Growing Older

Terrance N. James, PhD

 Poplar Publishing
Courtenay, BC, Canada

First published in 2010 by
Poplar Publishing
2766 O'Brien Road
Courtenay, B.C. V9N 9H9

Library and Archives Canada Cataloguing in Publication

James, Terrance N. (Terrance Norman), 1944-
Prader-Willi syndrome : growing older / written by Terrance N.
James.

Includes bibliographical references and index.
ISBN 978-0-9685838-1-4

1. Prader-Willi syndrome. 2. Prader-Willi syndrome--Patients--
Biography. 3. Prader-Willi syndrome--Patients--Care. 4. Aging--
Canada. I. Title.

RJ520.P7J25 2010   618.92'85884   C2010-901444-8

Cover photograph: Sproat Lake, Vancouver Island,
courtesy of Graham McMahon

Printed and bound in Canada by
Printorium Bookworks

Contents

1: Aging with developmental disabilities

2: Aging with Prader-Willi syndrome

3: Aging with PWS:
Some quality of life considerations

4: Aging parents

5: Profiles

6: An autobiography

7: Conclusion

List of figures

List of Tables

Preface

*P*rader-Willi Syndrome: Growing Older began as a chapter in
Prader-Willi Syndrome: Quality of Life (James, in press). The
matter of aging was one aspect of the follow-up study of individuals that
I had studied during doctoral research on social and psychological
aspects of Prader-Willi syndrome (PWS) in 1985/86. This involved
51 families in western Canada. After twenty years, I was interested
in tracking these people and exploring issues relating to their quality of life. During interviews, parents and caregivers expressed their
uncertainties about pragmatic aspects of aging with PWS, and the one
concern which weighed heaviest on their minds – the issue of future
care. I was encouraged by parents and guardians to pursue this topic in
more depth. It was evident from the literature that there had not been
any longitudinal studies, or even "snapshots," addressing the topic of
aging with PWS in Canada.

In exploring quality of life of older adults with PWS I was
constantly reminded of the importance of listening to them, to hear
their stories. While it was important to hear what parents, caregivers,
relatives and agency personnel had to say, it was even more compel-
ling to listen to what the adults with PWS were wanting to say. They
were all willing, and some very keen, to have their stories told. I hope
that this document respectfully reflects their voices.

Growing old is not something that we like to think about, for
ourselves or those we love. Yet aging is a reality that all must face.
Those with PWS recognize that they are aging, that they can't do
some of the things they used to be able do or that they can't remember
things as well any more. While parents and caregivers live with the
daily reminders of such aging with PWS, there is little professional
dialogue about aging and health, levels of care, or seniors activities
for those with PWS.

This document presents an overview of PWS and aging, and importantly contains profiles of individuals with PWS who have passed their fortieth birthday. While the sample is small, it is rich in description and testimony. It reflects current best practice from the point of view of those with PWS, their families and support workers.

What does it mean to be a senior with PWS in Canada today? Simply, we do not know. Over the next decade, however, the people profiled in this document will be more widely acknowledged as "seniors." Hopefully, the present material will help to understand the transition to this new status and be a catalyst to increase professional discussion.

Terrance James
May 2010

Acknowledgements

It takes strength of character to relate one's personal life story to others. The 13 individuals with PWS who consented to have their stories included in this book deserve much credit and applause for their willingness to tell their story in the interest of helping others. They deserve our collective thanks.

Thanks are also extended to those parents and caregivers who encouraged and supported research on the topic of aging with Prader-Willi syndrome. Their questions and concerns about future care and advocacy prompted this undertaking. Their time and effort in answering questions and later reviewing and editing profile drafts with their adult with PWS was greatly appreciated.

Another group of editors, those who were willing to read the entire manuscript and provide constructive feedback, must also be acknowledged. I am grateful for the editorial comments and corrections provided by Doris, Gillian, Joan and Colleen. Their efforts make this a more user-friendly document.

Dedicated to the individuals with PWS in the over-40 group, and their parents and caregivers, who contributed so generously to this project..

1

Aging with developmental disabilities

Canadians enjoy a high standard of living and longevity of life. All citizens benefit from a system of universal health care which gives equal access to needed medical services throughout their lifespan. Children's hospitals in each of the provinces provide high quality neonatal and childhood care.

People with disabilities are protected by the *Canadian Charter of Rights and Freedoms* (Government of Canada, 1984) and various forms of human rights legislation. Laws and social policies support the individual rights of people with disabilities.

The administration of social services is a provincial responsibility, which leads to variations across and within provinces. Today people with disabilities generally enjoy community living under a philosophical framework of normalization. In recent years a focus on client-centred services has fostered individualized programming in educational, residential and day programs.

While some of the seniors profiled in the current document spent many years in institutions, others did not. Most, however, received segregated special education experiences within public education. Today, school jurisdictions operate under a philosophy of inclusive education with a range of special education supports available to those with special needs.

Canada has a relatively small population and a very large territory. While there are large urban centres in every province, there are many small rural communities across the country. Geography can be a limiting factor in obtaining appropriate services for some families.

Marginalization of seniors with developmental disabilities

The National Advisory Council on Aging (2004), addressing aging in persons with developmental disabilities, identified factors which contribute to the marginalization of some seniors. Some with PWS will be affected by these factors in the same fashion as those with Down syndrome, Fragile X or any other developmental disability:

- differences in capacity may limit knowledge regarding disease prevention
- lack of experts available with knowledge of aging with developmental disabilities
- difficulties in communication
- lack of access to care and services in areas of physical and mental health (p. 3).

While these observations relate to seniors with developmental disabilities in general, they provide the context for parents and professionals to consider the needs of the aging adult with PWS.

There are still too few health professionals who have expertise in treating persons with developmental disabilities in general, and PWS in specific. This reality, combined with a lack of knowledge about the aging process and PWS, means that parents and siblings will continue their pioneering role as they advocate for services for a family member with PWS. They may also have to combat negative stereotyping and discriminatory attitudes from the public because of syndrome characteristics. Without such advocacy, seniors with PWS will experience marginalization like others with developmental disabilities.

Aging caregivers

Many adults with developmental disabilities enjoy the support of their family, however as they approach their senior years family members may no longer be able to provide care and advocacy. Parents may themselves require support. In some cases siblings step in to assume the roles previously played by the parents. Sometimes, however, parents anticipate new care requirements and make provisions to ensure that siblings do not have to carry the responsibility of future care.

Parents often profess their responsibility to care as a lifelong commitment - a burden to some, but not to others. They also express doubts about the ability of the social services systems to provide the levels of supports which they deem to be necessary.

In most cases, the decision is made to provide a community-based placement for a young adult with PWS, under the care of an agency or professional caregivers. What is anticipated as a long-term commitment to care for the individual, however, may have the same limitations as those experienced by parents. For example, advancing age, declining health and energy levels may require them to retire from their vocation as a caregiver, and to move into a different stage of life. Like parents, they often have the same uncertainties about the ability of the system to provide the needed level of care for the adult with PWS.

The Ontario Partnership on Aging and Developmental Disabilities (2007a), refers to the "dynamic of denial," the denial of a caregiver's own aging. The caregiver role cannot be exercised appropriately if there is denial. As a result of denial:

- the caregiver will not be prepared for any significant change in his/her care giving capacity due to aging
- the caregiver may avoid transition planning that acknowledges the aging of the individuals being supported
- the lack of planning, coupled with the inevitable aging of both the caregiver and the supported individual, may result in an inability to respond to a a crisis situation; the results may be circumstances where quality of life is compromised.

At best, the denial dynamic may provide a temporary extension of existing care; at worst, it delays transition planning and access to a continuum of services which should be available to everyone. Uncertainty about the roles and services of the seniors' system and disability system may feed into this dynamic of denial.

Disability system versus seniors system

Who should provide supports to seniors with disabilities? Should it be the disability system or the seniors system? In Canada, most individuals with developmental disabilities receive supports from the disability system throughout their life (Community Living Research Project, 2006). The report of the National Advisory Council on Aging (2004) notes that cooperation between the disability and seniors sectors in Canada is challenging. It identifies limited resources and a lack of knowledge and expertise with regard to seniors and disability as a cause. The disability services sector faces significant pressures from "the longer life expectancy of people being supported, the aging of family caregivers and the Aging Boom" (Ontario Partnership on Aging & Developmental Disabilities, 2007b). Within the disability system, the supported independent living and individualized day program models have enhanced the quality of life of most of the over-40 group with PWS.

By contrast, the seniors system commonly offers variations of congregate care, options that most of the over-40 group of adults with PWS would likely regard as unattractive. In other areas, however, the seniors system may offer advantages. For example, integrated recreation and leisure experiences may be attractive through seniors centres and discounted travel and restaurant services may offer financial savings.

While cooperation between the disability and seniors systems would be ideal, it remains an ideal to be achieved. In the meantime, parents, caregivers and advocates need to be creative in seeking out appropriate opportunities within both systems. Integration with seniors in general, however, may be difficult for the present generation. Today's seniors grew up when people with disabilities were institutionalized, hidden or denied acceptance and equality in the community.

Intellectual disabilities and dementia

According to Alzheimer's Disease International (2003), people with intellectual disabilities are living longer and healthier lives and are at increased risk of developing dementia. While the prevalence of dementia among people with intellectual disabilities is reported to be about the same as the general population there are also syndrome-specific anomalies. For example, the rate of Alzheimer disease (the most common cause of dementia), is reported to be about 25% for individuals with Down syndrome over age 40, and 65% beyond age 60. People with Down syndrome are "living longer and experiencing premature aging, specifically Alzheimer disease" (Kozma, 2008). There are no prevalence data for dementia or Alzheimer disease in individuals with PWS.

Are seniors with PWS at greater risk for dementia or Alzheimer disease?   Research from the field of neurobiology suggests that people who are overweight do have greater risk. For example, the risk of dementia is almost triple for those with central obesity (i.e. large abdominal girth) in their middle years (Whitmer et al., 2008).

Certainly, without intervention abdominal obesity is a common characteristic with PWS. Also, it has been shown that the presence of Type II diabetes, and the duration of the diabetes, are both related to cognitive decline in older men and women (Okerele et al., 2008). Adolescents and adults with PWS, left untreated, can become morbidly obese and at increased risk for diabetes mellitus, as well as other health issues (Stadler, 1995). It has been reported that approximately 30 % of morbidly obese individuals with PWS over the age of 20 have Type II diabetes. (Hanchett & Maier, 1995). While the presence of obesity and diabetes suggest the possibility of a higher rate of dementia and/or Alzheimer disease, PWS-specific research is needed to explore the reality.

Transition to senior status

Transition planning is an essential element in person-centred service systems, helping to maintain quality of life. It has been defined as "a deliberate, dynamic and conscious evolutionary process that supports the individual to embrace life as it presents itself during the aging process" (Ontario Partnership on Aging & Developmental Disabilities, 2007c). It addresses the uniqueness of individual circumstances, anticipating the next environment and the need for programs and services. It often involves a multi-disciplinary team, including family or advocates, along with the individual with PWS.

It is not clear how adults with PWS transition to senior status. The early literature suggested a decreased life expectancy that did not anticipate senior years; yet individuals with PWS in Canada are currently living into their fifth and sixth decades. Parents, caregivers and other service providers want to know what to anticipate with advancing age. Will adults with PWS experience an early onset or accelerated progression of aging? What changes can be expected in: activity levels, behaviour patterns, interpersonal relations, recreation-leisure interests, physical and mental health, and cognitive capacities? There are more questions than answers.

People aging with developmental disabilities require varying levels of support. Are there syndrome-specific correlates of aging unique to PWS which will have implications for the provision of effective supports? At the time of writing there is a paucity of literature exploring aging and the transition to senior status with PWS.

2

Aging with
Prader-Willi syndrome

For the purposes of the present document the term "seniors" refers to adults with PWS who have attained the age of 40 years. The Community Living Research Project (2006), in reviewing the literature on seniors with developmental disabilities, noted that the terms "senior" and "old age" vary across research studies and that "the cut-off age for determining senior status can begin as low as age 40" (p. 6). Age 40 is also the age at which the National Advisory Council on Aging (2004) suggests that annual medical check-ups are needed for people with disabilities.

At what point do individuals with PWS feel that they are seniors? At what point do friends, family and the community acknowledge them as seniors? And at what point does "the system" support them as seniors? While these questions are not directly answered in this document, it is hoped that the material contained herein will prompt discussion that will lead to a better understanding of PWS senior status and the supports required.

The senior PWS population

A review of major studies in the international literature revealed few studies with subjects over 50 years of age. The most recent report, by Waters, Jewson, Quinn, and Sharma (2007), a survey of members of the PWSA (UK), identified 26 adults with PWS over age 41, including four aged 51-55 and one aged 59 years. They reported age "41+" as the most senior age-band for analysis.

Other studies from the international literature identify upper ages which help to identify the aging population with PWS. An early

U.S. study by Greenswag (1987) reported an upper age of 64 years; a more recent study by Gunay-Aygun, Schwartz, Heeger, O'Riordan, and Cassidy (2001) found an upper age of 60. A prevalence study in Flanders (Vogels et al., 2004) cited an upper age of 56 years; a review from western Australia found an upper age of 48.3 (Thomson, Glasson, & Bittles, 2006). A national survey in Italy (Grugni, et al., 2008) had upper ages of 45.4 for males and 46.7 for females. The oldest individual PWS case report in the literature is a female of 71 years (Carpenter, 1994).

Presently there is no comprehensive national source for information on individuals with PWS in Canada. A survey of service providers in one region of Ontario in 2006 (Horvath), cited an upper age limit of 47 years. A similar survey in 2008 (PWS Network), found four individuals in the 45 to 54 age band, and two between ages 55 and 64. A survey of PWS families in Alberta (Kinash, 2007) cited an upper age of 54 years.

Table 1 presents the status of the over-40 group which is the subject of the present document. Data on 20 individuals over the age of 40 are included in this study. Ages for those living range from 40 to 57 years.

It is known that there was a backlog effect resulting in diagnoses of PWS during the adult years for some individuals, particu-

Table 1 Over-40 group status		
	Female	Male
Living	8	5
Deceased	4	3
Totals	12	8

larly prior to the late 1980s. But are there some older individuals as yet undiagnosed? Despite the frequency of infant diagnosis in the last 15 years, there are still some individuals who are not being diagnosed until the teen and young adult years. It is possible that some older adults with PWS have not been diagnosed.

The nature of a syndrome

A syndrome is a group of symptoms which generally occur together, producing a pattern typical of a particular disease. It is important to note that not all symptoms will necessarily be present, nor demonstrated to the same degree. In the case of PWS this is particularly true. For example, while most individuals with PWS are short of stature, there are some who are tall; while most have a mild or moderate degree of cognitive impairment there are some who are in the normal range for mental abilities and yet others who have a profound degree of impairment.

While it may be easy to generalize about a syndrome on the basis of quantifiable physical characteristics, it is more difficult to do so with personality and behaviour variables. Those with PWS demonstrate a wide range of interests, idiosyncrasies, talents, social skills and worker characteristics. While there may be some behavioural generalities which may hold true, the responses to individual situations are always unique.

PWS clinical characteristics

The first paper describing PWS was published by Prader, Labhart and Willi in 1956, under the title "A syndrome characterized by obesity, small stature, cryptorchidism and oligophrenia, following amyotonia-like status in infancy." So obesity, short stature, undescended testes, mental deficiency, and lack of muscle tone in infancy became the initial clinical standards for diagnosis. Within the next decade case reports of the new syndrome were published from several countries, including Canada. By 1979, more than 200 cases of PWS had been published internationally (Zellweger, 1981).

Differential diagnosis. Differential diagnosis during the neonatal period was difficult, particularly because hypotonia was common to a range of infant disorders. According to Cassidy (1984), diagnosis depended heavily on "clinical observation of physical stigmata and natural history." Variability and severity in the number of symptoms contributed to the difficulty with diagnosis. The differential diagnosis of PWS for older persons was more easily made on the basis of clinical findings and family history. By the 1980s, however, many General Practitioners still had never seen a case of PWS. Most diagnoses at that time were made by specialists.

Two phases. The early literature described two phases of PWS (Zelweger, 1981). Some of the first phase characteristics, such as the lack of muscle tone, poor sucking and swallowing reflex, poor weight gain, non-responsiveness, and delayed milestones were common to other abnormal developmental conditions and were thus confused or simply escaped recognition. Generally, it was not until the second phase characteristics, such as mental retardation, delayed psychomotor development, insatiable appetite, obesity, behavioural or emotional problems, and hypogonadism emerged and became troublesome that diagnosis was pursued and eventually made.

Research to practice gap. For many parents the gap between medical research knowledge and practice dictated a long ordeal of searching for information from doctors and other sources in order to satisfy their intuitive feelings that something was wrong with their child (Leconte, 1981). In some cases parents self-diagnosed the problem and then had to go about convincing medical doctors. By the late 1980s, James and Brown (1992) reported that parents in western Canada saw an average of six physicians, including General Practitioners and specialists, before receiving a diagnosis of PWS. The highest number of medical practitioners reportedly seen was 30, a figure given by a parent whose daughter had not been diagnosed until age 32. The research to practice gap has narrowed over the intervening years. Medical practitioners are more aware of PWS today, and are more likely to refer to specialists.

Consensus diagnostic criteria. It was not until 1993 that consensus diagnostic criteria were published identifying major, minor, and supportive features required for diagnosis of PWS (Holm, et al.). By the end of the decade, however, Smith (1999) noted that "a clinical diagnosis of PWS can be difficult to make with confidence." As PWS is a rare condition, many General Practitioners had still not seen a person with this disorder. For anyone currently 40 years of age or older, that is to say born prior to 1970, diagnosis was thus based on articles from an emerging literature which described an expanding number of clinical characteristics. Each of the individuals profiled in the current document received his or her diagnosis between 1960 and 1980, before the consensus diagnostic criteria were published.

The emergence of genetics

During the 1980s certain chromosomal findings, when coupled with obvious physical characteristics were resulting in earlier diagnoses than in the past. In 1986, Butler, Meaney, & Palmer, reported that approximately 50% of those studied cytogenetically (i.e., laboratory examination of a person's chromosomes by culture techniques) exhibited an abnormality of chromosome 15. Thereafter, genetic testing continued to refine and increase the possibility of diagnosis. Today genetic testing is routinely used for laboratory diagnosis of PWS. Gunay-Aygun et al. (2001) have proposed a less strict scoring system for the consensus diagnostic criteria in order to ensure that all appropriate candidates are tested.

Mis-classification

In a U.K. study of prevalence, birth, and mortality rates the authors (Whittington et al., 2001) asserted that "prior to the establishment of genetic criteria a proportion of all 'cases' were mis-classified" (p. 174). An American study, a retrospective examination of the charts of 90 patients with laboratory-confirmed PWS illustrates the difficulties associated with clinical assessment. The sensitivities of the major criteria ranged from only 49% for characteristic facial features to 98% for developmental delay. Sensitivities for eight of the minor criteria were higher than the sensitivity of characteristic facial features, which is a major criterion. Most importantly, 15 out of the 90 patients with molecular diagnosis did not meet the clinical diagnostic criteria (Gunay-Aygun et al., 2001). Clearly clinical assessment is a subjective process which leaves room for error.

Issues in diagnosis for older persons

The mis-classification difficulties associated with clinical assessment can be of two types, under-diagnosis or over-diagnosis. Under-diagnoses may have occurred due to lack of awareness or inconsistent interpretation of the physical and behavioural characteristics, largely on the part of General Practitioners. On the other hand, over-diagnoses might have occurred for the same reasons. Also, there could have been additional pressures to diagnose when eligibility for services depended on the diagnostic label. These possibilities are important when considering the older PWS population.

From the 1960s through the 1980s the backlog effect resulted in many diagnoses during the teen and adult years. Although genetic testing is now readily available, it does not seem important for older individuals with clinically diagnosed PWS. In fact, only three of the individuals profiled in the present document have a genetic confirmation of PWS. Simply, it is not seen as relevant at this stage of life given that services and supports are stable. Any additional information that further testing might reveal would not likely contribute to a change in the quality of life.

Are there still older individuals with PWS who have not yet been diagnosed? The example of Bob in the next section illustrates the uncertainties related to diagnosis of an older person and suggests that there may still be seniors with PWS who have never been diagnosed.

PWS or PWS-like?

Today some individuals who present with many of the clinical characteristics of PWS, but fail to receive genetic confirmation, are
considered to be "PWS-like." Similarly, some who, as a result of head
trauma or brain tumour, have demonstrated the acquired characteristics of food preoccupation, obesity and behavioural issues similar to
PWS, may be described with the same term. From the parent and
caregiver perspective, association with a support group sympathetic
to, and knowledgeable about, the symptoms is positive. Whether PWS
is confirmed, or not, may not be relevant. What is important is the
support received to manage the problematic behaviours associated
with daily living.

The case of Bob. Bob was born in 1941 and spent his younger
years as a resident of Woodlands and Tranquille, British Columbia's
institutions for the "mentally retarded" of the period. At age 30 he was
placed in a large rural group home facility run by a church-sponsored
organization providing supports for adults with developmental
disabilities. Bob displayed some common PWS food behaviours, (e.g.,
raiding the fridge, taking food from the pantry, searching for food in
garbage containers, sneaking food from others, hoarding food under
his bed), obesity (BMI greater than 35.0) and excessive daytime som-
nolence (e.g., sleeping after eating, sleeping when riding in a car). His
food related behaviours persisted across environments, that is to say
in the group home, at work and at church. As a consequence, he
was treated by the house parents as if having PWS.

For 12 years, from age 30 to 42, interventions for Bob included
restricted access to food, diet control, daily exercise, and strict supervision. His weight reduced from 260 to 210 pounds over this time
period. However, there was never a medical diagnosis of PWS. Bob
was in good health and seldom needed medical attention.

With a change in group home management, Bob and the other
residents were given a less restrictive environment. Gradually he
was allowed to make food choices and to help himself to food items
from the fridge. The new manager came to believe that Bob didn't
necessarily have PWS, but rather just a "healthy appetite" for food,
and that he would sneak food due to the many years of restrictions that
he had experienced. Having food available seemed to take away the
necessity of hoarding. Garbage containers in the yard, however, were
kept locked for reasons of health and safety. Bob's weight did increase
with this more relaxed approach.

Today, at age 68, Bob lives in a private care home with experienced caregivers. He is described as having a placid personality, and no major behavioural issues. He no longer requires oxygen for his sleep apnea. He still has a healthy appetite, but does not obsess over food. He is six feet tall and maintains his weight at 220 pounds. He is described as having a healthy constitution and takes medications only for high cholesterol and a thyroid condition.

Does Bob have PWS? There is insufficient file information to retrospectively apply the diagnostic criteria and no urgency to do genetic testing at his age. Could the changes in residential environments and caregiver routines account for some of the changes in food-related behaviours? Could it be that Bob's behaviours have mellowed with advancing age? Or could it be that his height did not fit the common stereotype of PWS and thus excluded the possibility of this diagnosis?

Tall stature. While short stature appeared as one of the cardinal features of PWS in the original work by Prader et al. (1956), it is only a minor criterion in the consensus diagnostic criteria for PWS published in 1993 (Holm et al.). Tall stature can be an atypical characteristic (Harty, Hollowell, & Sieg, 1993), although relatively rare. One young man from Alberta, with genetic confirmation, was short when compared to sibling height, but measured just over six feet tall. Tall stature should not rule out the possibility of PWS if other clinical characteristics are present.

Genetic testing

The deletion on chromosome 15, which accounts for about 70% of PWS cases, was first reported in 1981 (Ledbetter et al.). By 1983 it was determined that the chromosome 15 deletion was in the chromosome 15 inherited from the father (Butler & Palmer). In 1989, the observation of maternal uniparental disomy (UPD, i.e., both chromosome 15s from the mother) was first reported (Nicholls, Knoll, Butler, Karam, & Lalande). The improvements in genetic testing techniques during the 1980s laid the foundation for earlier and more reliable diagnoses.

The two most common chromosome errors, paternal deletion (70%) and maternal UPD (25%), can occur in any conception, that is to say that PWS is not inherited in these instances. Imprinting defects, which occur in less than 5 percent of the cases, can be inherited (Keuder, 2005). As mentioned earlier, all the individuals profiled in this document were diagnosed clinically between 1960 and 1980, before the availability of genetic testing. Unless the clinical diagnosis of PWS was later in question there would have been no need for genetic testing during the adult years.

It was difficult to ascertain whether the individuals in this over-40 group had ever undergone genetic testing. Some parents could not recall with certainty that testing had been done, others thought that it might have been done but didn't know the results. In some cases parents were deceased and family members did not know if testing had been performed. Only three parents confirmed the chromosome 15 deletion; none identified maternal UPD.

Gender differences

Prader-Willi syndrome affects males and females equally (Alexander, Van Dyke & Hanson, 1995). Are there gender differences, however, in the senior PWS population? The oldest case reports in the literature are all of females, ages 65 (Greenswag, 1988), 68 (Butler, 2000), 69 (Goldman, 1988) and 71 (Carpenter, 1994). Whether the reporting of elderly females reflected a genuine sex difference or an artefact of survey techniques was unclear according to Carpenter. Recently, Waters et al. (2007) reported an even split in the 26 individuals over age 41 in the U.K. The present study presents a 60:40 split in favour of females.

Life expectancy

There are two ways to consider life expectancy according to Statistics Canada (2007). Traditionally, "life expectancy" is

> the number of years a person would be expected to live, starting at birth if the age- and sex- specific mortality rates for a given observation period (such as a calendar year) were held constant over the estimated life span.

According to this measure, in 2001 Canadian males could expect to live 76.9 years and females 82.0 years. The "health-adjusted life expectancy," however, may be a more relevant comparison when discussing PWS. By introducing the concept of quality of life, it is a more comprehensive life-expectancy measure.

> Health adjusted life expectancy is the number of years in full health that an individual can expect to live given the current morbidity and mortality conditions.

Using this measure, in 2001 Canadian males could expect to live 68.3 years and females 70.8 years.

Longevity. The literature "consistently asserts that the life expectancy of individuals with a disability continues to rise as health and social conditions continue to improve" (Community Living Project, 2006, p. 11). It is reasonable to expect that individuals with PWS, like others with developmental disabilities, will live longer in the future. A Medical Reference Guide issued by the International Prader-Willi Syndrome Organization (IPWSO, n.d.) indicates that life expectancy for those with PWS "may be normal if weight is controlled" (p. 2), although "survival past the fifth or sixth decade is unusual" according to Eiholzer and Lee (2006, p. 98). Assuming early identification and management consistent with current knowledge and best practices, there can be optimism that younger individuals with PWS can live into their senior years.

Mortality rates. In a longitudinal Australian study, Einfeld et al. (2006) determined that deaths in the PWS population occurred at a rate 20 times greater than in control groups with mild intellectual disability or average IQ. They found no significant differences in mortality rates relative to the genetic type of PWS or gender, however this may have been due to the small sample size. There are no published mortality rates for the Canadian PWS population.

Survivor effect. In a study from the United Kingdom, Waters et al. (2007) describe sharp increases in BMI and obesity levels after age twenty, leading to increased mortality from obesity-related diseases in the late twenties and thirties. They suggest that adults with the most severe weight problems may succumb to obesity-related diseases at an earlier age than those who have been able to control their weight. They speculate that there is a "survivor effect" among older adults with PWS, those in their late 30s and beyond. They suggest that older age groups can be expected to contain a higher proportion of people with PWS who, for whatever reasons, did not experience as serious and/or as prolonged weight problems as others of their peers.

The data for the over-40 individuals profiled in the present document do not support the interpretation by Waters et al. (2007). The weight data suggest that most had experienced an extreme level of life threatening obesity at some time earlier in their lives. Ten out of the 13 individuals profiled in the current document had BMIs in excess of 40 during their third or fourth decades. The highest BMIs were 74.3, 64.6, and 62.8. Their weight histories are equal to, or more serious than, other peers who died. This suggests that the survivor effect may be based on factors other than low weight maintenance, or short duration of weight problems, in the twenties and thirties. According to their testimonies, they are survivors due to a range of factors, including: change of residence, degree of independence, desire to change, minimal house rules, involvement in menu planning and food preparation, choices in activities planning, a trusted coach/mentor, structured weigh-ins, and social reinforcement. These require more research, along with more standard enquiry to explore such topics as: healthy lifestyles, the timeliness of interventions, diet and exercise management practices, inherited constitution and longevity characteristics, and the consistency and type of additional supports provided.

Age at diagnosis

The average age of diagnosis for females profiled in the current document was 15.4 years, while males were diagnosed much earlier at 1.75 years. Age of diagnosis was unknown for one male. The age range at diagnosis for females was 5 – 26 years. In the U.K., Waters et al. (2007) found an average age of diagnosis for the 41+ group to be 18.4 years. They did not report diagnostic information by gender. Their range for diagnosis went from less than 12 months to 42 years.

A review of the ages at diagnosis for the under-40 and over-40 PWS groups in the author's files shows little change for males, but a marked decline for females since 1986, as seen in Table 2. The mean of 2.39 years for the post- 1986 females is skewed by four diagnoses (5, 8, 12, and 18 years).

Table 2 Age at diagnosis (in years)		
Year	Male	Female
Pre-1986	mean = 3.66 range = 1 - 19 n =14	mean = 9.12 range = <1 - 32 n = 25
Post-1986	mean = 3.63 range = <1 - 13 n = 12	mean = 2.39 range = <1 - 12 n = 19

With these removed, the average would be slightly more than one month. Today parents often receive the diagnosis of PWS before their infant leaves the hospital.

Height

Short stature was one of the characteristics identified by Prader et al. (1956) in the first publication on this syndrome. "Short stature for genetic background by age 15" is one of the minor diagnostic criteria for PWS (Holm et al. 1993).

Group similarity. Heights for the over-40 group ranged from 4'6" (137.16 cm) to 5'0" (152.4 cm) for females and 4'10" (147.32 cm) to 5'5" (165.1 cm) for males. The tallest of the males, however, had received growth hormone treatment. These heights fall within the parameters described for PWS adults, and at less than the 5th percentile for the regular population (Butler & Meaney, 1991).

Growth hormone (GH). Prior to 1985, GH was prepared from animal and human cadaver sources. Thereafter synthetic GH became available. In 1995, GH replacement therapy for adults received regulatory approval in the U.S.A. and in Europe. Safety and efficacy trials delayed approval for use in childhood PWS (with growth failure) until 2000 (Carrel, Lee, & Mozul, 2006).

The one individual in the present study who benefitted from GH treatment in 1975, at age 10, received it from a pediatrician who had just returned from a seminar with Dr. Hans Zellweger, an international pioneer in the field of medical genetics with a particular interest in Prader-Willi syndrome.

Weight

Obesity is universally acknowledged as a health risk factor. It can also be a factor in self-concept and social acceptance. How do those aging with PWS manage their weight?

Weight variability. Current weights for the individuals profiled in this book ranged from 123 to 239 pounds (55.35 to 107.55 kg). This coincided with the range for females. Males ranged from 152 to 183 pounds (68.4 to 87.35 kg). The average weight for females was 168.8 pounds (75.97 kg); the average weight for the males was 163.25 pounds (73.46 kg).

The average of the highest-ever weights for females was 247 pounds (112.04 kg), with a highest weight of 300 pounds (136 kg); the average of the highest-ever weights for males was 284.4 pounds (129 kg), with a highest weight of 368 pounds (166.9 kg). None of the highest-ever weights occurred after age 40.

Within the last 12 months 9 out of 13 lost weight, ranging from 2 to 34 pounds (an average of 13.2 pounds or 5.98 kg). For two individuals weight was maintained without appreciable change. There was incomplete data for the other two individuals.

Body mass index. Body mass index (BMI) is calculated by dividing an individual's weight (in kilograms) by height (in metres) squared.

Table 3 shows the distribution of the over-40 group BMIs according to the World Health Organization (2006) classification system. One-quarter of the participants had BMIs under 30. Of the 75% who were in the obese range, three were considered to be morbidly obese, that is with

Table 3 Over-40 group current BMIs			
BMI	Classification	No.	%
under 18.5	underweight	0	0.0
18.5 to 24.9	normal	2	16.6
25.0 to 29.9	pre-obese	1	8.3
30 to 34.9	obese Class I	5	41.7
35 to 39.9	obese Class II	2	16.7
over 40	obese Class III	3	16.7

BMIs over 40. In 2004, 23% of the general Canadian population had BMIs in the obese range (i.e., >30) (Statistics Canada, 2008).

In a cross-cultural comparison of obesity in PWS, Dudley et al. (2008) cite the following rates for BMIs greater than 30: France 82.5%, Belgium 65.8%, U.S.A. 58.2% and U.K. 54.3%. These rates, however, are for the general PWS adult populations, not specifically senior populations. Dykens (2004) found a mean BMI of 34.01 for 30 to 50 year old Americans with PWS.

Table 4 BMI comparison: Canadian & UK seniors		
	UK	Canada
average	36.9	33.1
maximum	70.2	57.6

A comparison of BMIs for Canadian and U.K. seniors with PWS can be seen in Table 4. The average and maximum BMIs are lower in the Canadian group when compared to the group reviewed by Waters et al. (2007).

Morbid obesity. Obesity leads to medical complications. Morbid obesity simply refers to the state of obesity where the body has become unhealthy and at risk for physical disability and consequently an impaired quality of life. Morbid obesity is generally defined as a BMI greater than 40.

Risk of developing health problems may also be associated with age, inherited traits and presence or absence of other conditions. The home environment in which an individual is raised, for example, may include poor eating habits, physical inactivity, and tobacco use which might predispose an individual to repeating the same patterns in their adult life. As Christensen and Hainline (2001) point out, "obesity is a multifactorial condition with both genetic and environmental components" (p. 4).

Obesity-related diseases. The most prevalent obesity-related diseases include: heart disease, diabetes (type II), high blood pressure, stroke, orthopedic problems, sleep apnea, and cancer (Christensen

& Hainline, 2001). Eiholzer and Lee (2006) identify respiratory insufficiency or cardiorespiratory failure as the major cause of overall mortality in PWS and point out that "in many cases, demise appears to be triggered by acute or chronic pulmonary infection" (p. 99). According to Cassidy and Schwartz (2009), "obesity-related cardiovascular problems and gastric causes or sleep apnea" are the most frequent causes of death in adults. "Other causes of morbidity include diabetes mellitus, thrombophlebitis, and skin problems (e.g., chronic edema, infection from skin picking)."

Decline in morbid obesity with advancing age. At a BCPWSA conference in Vancouver, Heinemann (2008) presented PWSA-USA data which showed that morbid obesity (i.e., BMI >40) declines with advancing age. A comparison of BMI data from ages 19 to 34 with ages 35 and up showed a marked decline of those in the morbidly obese category, from 34% to 16% in these two groups respectively. Two reasons were speculated for this observation. Those who were morbidly obese as younger adults may not have survived beyond age 35, and those who were over the age of 35 were more likely to be in a care facility where they would get better nutritional management.

The BMI data for the over-40 group in this book challenge both of Heinemann's assumptions. Eleven out of 14 seniors (78.5%) for whom earlier weight data were available were morbidly obese (BMI range: 40 to 74.3) as younger adults and survived. And while better nutritional management might well be a factor in survival, it is not necessarily because of placement in a care facility. Four individuals live with family, seven live in supported independent living arrangements, one lives in a PWS group home and another in private residence with caregivers. If Heinemann's speculation is valid for the American PWS population, then more subtle differences related to residential models and dietary management may be at play in Canada.

Weekly weight data. Weekly weigh-ins are required for several of the over-40 group. This is a practice which began many years earlier. The charts are used for monitoring by staff and parents.

Weekly weigh-in data for one woman, gathered for more than 25 years, allows for a comparison of weight across residential models. Each bar in Figure 1 represents a different residence, in chronological order over a seven year period. While the length of time in each residence varied, weight was averaged for the entire duration of each situation. Weight was best controlled in the

"Behaviour Group Home" where all residents were strictly managed according to principles of applied behaviour analysis. The
weight data for this placement covered a period of 30 months. In
contrast, weight was highest during a three month period of
hospitalization, where the woman had been admitted at 247 pounds
suffering from heart failure. She had been living at home at the time.
Over the next seven years she had eight residential placements. The
average weights calculated for six of these placements, including
parents' home, integrated group homes and supported independent
living experiences were almost identical. All of these placements
occurred while the subject was in her twenties and included her highest ever weights. Today, in her forties she maintains her weight at
about 170 pounds (77 kilograms), slightly less than for most of her
placements in her twenties.

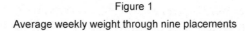

Figure 1

Average weekly weight through nine placements

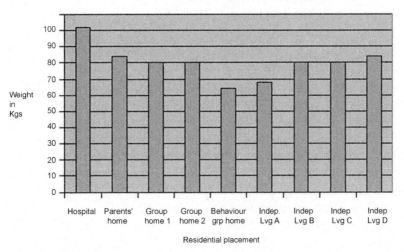

For one male weight data was gathered daily. The routine was
self-administered, initialled by staff and submitted to the parents.
The weight was converted to a BMI value and used to keep their son
within the "normal" category (18.5 - 24.9). The rigour of the weight
data routines has helped their son to remain within the normal range
throughout his adult years.

Weekly weigh-ins can also provide clues to other behavioural
concerns. One mother explained that the weekly weigh-ins over many

years allowed for analysis of her son's ups and downs, revealing that "binges coincided with stresses in his life such as holiday baking season."

Diets

Diet management is an essential intervention with PWS. The *Red Yellow Green System for Weight Management* (Balko, 2005), based on the metaphor of a stoplight, is widely promoted through parent organizations. Green "go" (low calorie), yellow "caution" (moderate calorie) and red "stop" (high calorie) foods and serving sizes are identified, and individuals are empowered to construct balanced diets within their caloric targets.

Diet management practices for the over-40 group ranged from strict external controls (in private care homes and group homes) to full participation in menu planning, grocery shopping, and meal preparation (in supported independent living and some family living environments). The most important element in diet management, from the perspective of the individual with PWS, is the ability to have some choices and control.

Strict calorie counting, perhaps the most rigorous approach to diet, was reported by four homes. Calorie goals ranged from 900 to 1200 daily. The diabetic exchange system, which gives latitude in choice making and control was reported in three homes. Only one home was committed to the Red Yellow Green diet. Another utilized the Weight Watchers diet. A few parents/caregivers professed knowledge of, and/or experience with, the structured approaches of calorie counting and food exchange systems and combined elements from these approaches with strong interest in nutrition and exercise in an eclectic approach. Only one family reported that they just ate "regular meals," with no special dietary considerations. All individuals with PWS reported satisfaction with diet management practices in their current living situations, although some were critical of practices in earlier living environments.

A daily multivitamin (Balko, 2005) and mineral supplements have been highly recommended for individuals with PWS (Scheimann, Lee & Ellis, 2006).

Environmental controls

Environmental controls are used primarily to restrict access to food. The following are common strategies observed in the residential situations of this over-40 group.

Use of locks. When asked about locks there was a range of responses. One woman reported that she felt more secure knowing that the fridge and cabinets were locked; another said that locks made her feel like she was in jail. When used, locks commonly prevent entry to the kitchen or pantry area. Alternatively, they are used to secure individual food storage cabinets, refrigerators and freezers. Locks were generally discrete. Nobody was using a chain and padlock around a fridge. Locks are considered essential for food management in the PWS-specific group home model.

Limited access to kitchen. Limited access to the kitchen usually means that access is only permitted with supervision. This is more common in group living or private care situations. Restricting access to the kitchen, however, is contrary to the concept of independent living. If there is full kitchen access, there is more likely to be locked food storage.

Door alarms. Door alarms are used primarily to monitor activity during the night hours in independent living situations. In one case, the individual has a private apartment in an agency-owned residential building. The alarms allow for night staff to monitor any entry and exit from individual units. In another situation, the alarm permits the live-in staff to be alerted if the person with PWS leaves her bedroom at night.

Strategic location. One caregiver explained how locating a bedroom away from traffic flow to the kitchen, and situating a day program activity away from the traffic lane to the lunchroom, were both meant to reduce temptation and the opportunity to access food. Similarly, a parent described how it was important to strategically choose a restaurant table away from the view of the kitchen door, where waitresses might be seen delivering food, or out of view of the dessert display or buffet table. Placement of the individual to be looking out of a window or at a wall was also used as a distraction. Such examples are meant to reduce the impact of the presence of food stimuli.

Site modification. Site modifications are more likely to be undertaken when the facility is owned by a family or an agency. For example, one home had the kitchen divided into a food preparation area and an eating area. The food area, including fridge, stove and food storage cabinets, was separated from the dining area by a lockable door. A small fridge in the eating area was available for unsupervised use when the mother was away. Other site modifications have created: a staff sleeping area, elevated food storage, and mobility supports.

Control of money. All of the individuals in the over-40 group understand the purchasing power of money. Some had abused their access to money in the past and had restrictions as a result. Some had no access to money; all of their affairs were managed for them. Others had the use of money on approval of the caregiver, and only for a specific planned purpose. When activities were done without supervision, receipts were necessary as an accountability measure. No one had an independent bank account, although some had accounts with a co-signer.

Supervision. Supervision ranged from 24/7 care involving several staff on rotation, to no agency supervision at all. The highest level of supervision was provided for persons in the supported independent living model where 24/7 attendant care was required. A variation on this model provided one-to-one for an individualized day program, but shared supervision at night in an agency care facility. In another case a group home and workshop program provided shared supervision. For one individual this was supplemented by one-on-one time for leisure activities.

In the three situations where individuals were living with family, the levels of support varied. In one case there was supervision for an individualized day program, in another there was supervision at a workshop program, and in the third case there was no supervision beyond that provided by the family.

Cognitive abilities

The diagnostic criteria for PWS include "cognitive disabilities, usually mild mental retardation," through adulthood (PWSA-USA, 2008). According to Whitman and Greenswag (1995), "all persons with PWS have some cognitive limitations" (p. 127). When PWS was first identified, "mental retardation" was the accepted term. This was later replaced with "mental handicap." According to the Canadian Association for Community Living (2008), preferred terms today are "intellectual disability" and "developmental disability."

Intellectual disabilities. In a U.K. study, Whittington et al. (2004) found a "near normal distribution of FSIQ [full scale intelligence quotient] scores for the PWS population," with a "shift of the ability distribution downwards by about 40 IQ points." The near normal distribution underscores that there is a range within PWS. They found all ability subscales were affected, suggesting "a global, rather than specific effect on cognition" (p. 182).

Whitman and Greenswag (1995) asserted that there are often "learning and language disabilities in addition to a global slowness" (p. 127). In other words, difficulties may be in the form of a learning disability and/or cognitive impairment. Either one will likely create difficulty in coping with the demands of daily activities throughout the lifespan.

Whittington et al. (2004) suggested that intellectual abilities of children and adults with PWS may be masked by their immature social behaviour. Feedback from parents and guardians of the over-40 group did not identify immature social behaviour as an issue. To the contrary, they pointed out the appropriateness of social behaviours when going out for coffee, attending dances, or hanging out with friends. It may be the case, however, that intellectual abilities are masked in other ways. For example, characteristics such as low energy, immature speech, and poor impulse control may lead to an underestimate of intellectual ability. On the other hand, high verbal skill, good reading ability and appropriate etiquette may lead to an over-estimate of intellectual functioning. Although descriptions of well-orchestrated food seeking behaviours, sometimes utilizing multi-step procedures, are not usually suggestive of a mental handicap, psychological assessment generally places most individuals with PWS in the mild to moderate range of intellectual functioning.

Genetic subtypes. In 1999 Dykens, Cassidy and King reported higher full-scale IQ scores for a group of UPD subjects when compared to a matched deletion subgroup. The following year, Roof et al. (2000) found subjects with UPD had significantly higher verbal IQ scores (an average of 9.1 points). This study is important because the average verbal IQ of the UPD group was 69.9 and the cut-off point for the classification of mild mental retardation by the American Psychiatric Association (APA) is IQ 70. Only 17% of the deletion group subjects had a score of 70 or higher, while 50% of the UPD group met or exceeded this point. As the authors suggest, this "carries substantial implications for individual classification, placement and service decisions" (p. 79). The APA classification is used as a basis for service in many jurisdictions. Indeed, a 2008 decision by the Government of British Columbia to include "a score of 70 or less" in the definition of developmental disability (Province of

B.C., 2008) may leave some families with a PWS member without services through Community Living B.C.

Visual-perceptual skills. The same study by Roof et al. (2000), found a significant strength for the deletion group in object assembly, a performance test measuring visual-perceptual skills. In 2002, Dykens reported that individuals with PWS demonstrated relative strength at standardized visual-spatial tasks, scoring at a par with normal peers on word searches and far outperforming them on jigsaw puzzles, placing more than twice as many pieces This puzzle proficiency was predicted by genetic type, with those of the deletion variety being most skilled.

Within the over-40 group, the three individuals with confirmed deletion were all keen to do jig-saw puzzles (up to 2500 pieces). Others in the group had little or no interest in jig-saw puzzles, but were considered to be verbally high functioning. Whittington et al. (2001) found higher verbal abilities in the disomy group, but a particular difficulty with coding (visual-motor coordination, motor and mental speed).

Receptive vocabulary. Receptive language was identified by Levine and Wharton (1993) as a learning strength for children with PWS. That is to say that children tend to be better at understanding language than expressing it. If this is so, adults may benefit from continued opportunities for language-based learning.

The PPVT-R (Peabody Picture Vocabulary Test - Revised) was administered by James (1987; James & Brown, 1992) to subjects with PWS in western Canada as a quick assessment of verbal ability. The scattergram of PPVT-R scores suggested a group pattern of performance decline with advancing age. Four of the individuals from the over-40 group were re-administered the same PPVT-R instrument in 2007. In two out of the four cases, the age equivalent scores increased by more than 2.5 years over the 20 year period. In the first case, the individual enjoyed a stimulating home environment where she engaged in language-based activities such as reading food labels, books, magazines and piano music. In the second case the individual did crossword puzzles and word searches on a daily basis, and kept abreast of current events in the news. In the other two cases there was a marginal loss and a marginal increase. Maintaining a language-rich environment in the adult years may help to delay declines in cognitive performance.

Memory. According to Levine and Wharton (1993), long term memory for information is also a relative strength for children with PWS. By contrast, short term auditory memory was identified as a learning weakness. But what is the experience of older adults? At 40, one woman was engaging in memory work as she was taking academic upgrading. Another was described as having a "good memory." On the other hand, one parent reported that her daughter was having increased difficulties with memory and understanding. She cited forgetfulness in taking medications and needles. Another caregiver reported that she is "observing the beginning of cognitive loss in certain areas, i.e., memory." Another commented that "memory is a little harder now" for her daughter. Two individuals with PWS, one male and one female, expressed concern for their own forgetfulness.

Behaviour

Behaviour problems are identified as a minor criterion for PWS (Holm et al., 1993). They include "temper tantrums, violent outbursts and obsessive/compulsive behavior; tendency to be argumentative, oppositional, rigid, manipulative, possessive, and stubborn; perseverating, stealing, and lying." Five or more of these symptoms are required in order to count toward diagnosis. There is ample evidence in parent support materials to confirm that behaviour is one of the more difficult management aspects of PWS. There is little, however, addressing behaviours of older persons with PWS.

Maladaptive behaviours studies. In the U.K., Clarke, Boer, Chung, Sturney, and Webb (1996) compared 30 adults with PWS to 30 adults with non-specific learning disability and suggested that temper tantrums, self injury, impulsiveness, lability of mood, inactivity and repetitive speech are characteristic behaviours in PWS in adult life. Dykens (2004) compared 45 adults with PWS (ages 30-50) with 195 children, adolescents and young adults with PWS and found that maladaptive and compulsive symptoms diminished significantly in older adults. However Clarke et al. (2002) reported that compulsive symptoms did not decline with age.

Testimonial evidence from parents and guardians of the over-40 group suggests that there is a broad range in behaviours that might be considered to be maladaptive and that individuals display varying severity of these behaviours. In interviews conducted by the writer with younger age groups, the topic of maladaptive behaviours consumed proportionately more interview time. No one in the over-40 group was in crisis due to behaviours at the time of interviews. Only two people reported crises during the last twelve months. In both cases they occurred in work environments.

Mellowing with age. Dykens (2004) found that adults with PWS (30 to 50 years) seemed to "mellow" behaviourally with age. Specifically, she was referring to less skin-picking, compulsiveness and non-compliant behaviours. Mellowing suggests a reduced frequency and intensity of behaviour episodes over time. The phrase "mellowing with age" has been used by parents to describe a change in behaviour which is in contrast to behaviours which occurred at a younger age. For example, one mother of a 27-year-old described a mellowing in her daughter who had moved into a group home. In contrast to the rough times that they had shared during the teen years, they enjoyed visits every other weekend when the daughter wasn't too busy. Both enjoyed the new and better relationship. However, is this true mellowing as a result of increasing age, or is it a function of living in a different environment and no longer being under the direct supervision of the parent?

At age 40, one woman's behaviour is said to have changed for the better. Similarly, at 55 another is said to be more relaxed, less anxious and not as easily upset as in earlier years. In both cases those closest to these women suggest that the change in behaviour is most likely a function of their more independent lifestyles in recent years rather than true mellowing due to age. On the other hand, another woman at age 44, was described as being more mellow and better able to tolerate crises, while living with her family. Similarly, another mother reported that her daughter now has a better understanding of situations. "Her anger dissipates easier now," she says, and then adds "yes, both of us are mellowing." Another woman who was hospitalized and sedated almost annually (for one to four weeks) before age 40 has not had this necessity in the last five years. Again, it is not certain if this is a true mellowing or the result of a change of guardianship and a move into a supported independent living model, or a combination of such factors. The profiles of two of the males also indicate improvements in behaviour. In both cases, however, the improvements are said to be due to medications according to family members.

The behaviours for the over-40 group, as described by families, are generally more mellow at the current ages than in earlier years. It is difficult to know, however, if it is a true mellowing or a function of the residential situation, management procedures or medications.

Hypotheses for mellowing behaviours. Dykens (2004) provides three possible hypotheses for the "sweeping, across-the-board drops in behavioural difficulties" in older adults with PWS:

- selective survival issues (those who live longer show fewer obesity-related medical problems and may do better behaviourally as well)
- unknown hormonal or physiological factors
- benefits of years of sustained behavioural and dietary interventions.

In talking about their own behaviours, some of the over-40 group recognized a positive change. They connected better behaviour to quality of life factors such as: independence, personal planning, choice making, supportive programs and personnel, adult respect, and meaningful relationships. They attributed fewer problematic behaviours to their more normalized circumstances.

Food related behaviours. From an early age, food is the trigger for many behavioural issues. Food has been described as a "preoccupation" and a "driving force." For some mothers it is the perseveration on food, the incessant repetition of questions related to when the next meal will occur, or what it will be, that is constant and annoying. Some individuals engage in undesirable behaviours to actually obtain food: food-seeking, foraging, and stealing. And then there are the behaviours having to do with what happens when the individual has obtained food: the hiding/concealing of food, the clandestine consumption, or the gorging or regurgitation habits.

The need for food access controls is well established with the over-40 group. While there were some food episodes described, they were handled in routine ways. In some cases there was a response cost (e.g., giving up a treat, smaller next portion); in other cases there were no appreciable consequences. Generally, controls were in place to preclude food access. There was more positive than negative discussion related to food and behaviours. Sympathetic parents and caregivers gave examples of success when temptation or the opportunity to sneak food was high.

Food and self-control. Are individuals with PWS capable of exercising self-regulating behaviours in the presence of food? While parents and caregivers provided examples of self-control, most of these occurred in the presence of witnesses. For example, they cited eating appropriately at a smorgasbord, buffet or pot-luck. In such circumstances, however, someone was providing supervision. Kinash's Alberta study (2007) included two women and one man over 41 who felt "that perhaps the food drive was not as all-consuming [as] it once had been" (p. 40).

In two cases in the over-40 group, individuals living in the home of their parents were able to stay unsupervised on their own for several days at a time. In one case, the kitchen was locked and the apportioned food was available in a small fridge in the dining area; in the other case the individual had full run of the kitchen,

Kinash (2007) points out that the distinction between the "physiological state of hunger" (i.e., the hunger drive) and the "psychological trigger of food salience" (i.e., the presence of food) is an important consideration. Understanding the difference will help to determine the best way to support persons with PWS. She goes on to explain that frequent low-calorie high nutrient foods and coping strategies are necessary for people who are constantly hungry, where-as minimizing food sights, smells and sounds in the environment is appropriate to address the issue of food salience. When food and re-lated food stimuli are minimized in the environment some individuals with PWS in the over-40 group are capable of attending to task, being quite productive and not preoccupied with food.

Kitchen privileges. Should seniors with PWS be permitted kitchen privileges? Parents and caregivers have differing philo-sophical positions on this matter. The advocates of family living or semi-independent living generally support some kitchen privileges. Individuals may have limited kitchen access, or they may be totally involved in meal planning, shopping and food preparation. It is argued that involvement requires choice making and fosters a sense of self control. Limited access may mean "only with supervision" or it may mean access to a limited amount of food items, for example drinks and low calorie snacks available in a small fridge. Kitchen privileges are most often denied in highly structured group living situations where professional staff are responsible for all meal preparation and where there is an emphasis on total food access control.

Living status. Dykens (2004) reported that living status was found to be a predictor of problems for adults, and that there were "sweeping declines in problems among older adults." Parents and care-givers of the over-40 group described improvements in relationships once the adult with PWS moved out of the family home, regardless of the type of placement. Even one individual who was resistant to moving from the family home eventually experienced improved relationships with his parents. A stable living environment outside of the parents' home seems to contribute to a sense of independence, self-worth and behavioural improvement for most adults with PWS.

Physical health

It is sometimes difficult to distinguish between illnesses which are age-related and those which are syndrome-related. Loss of energy, reduction in strength and endurance, and memory loss, for example, may be normal correlates of aging. Obesity, a high risk of cardio-vascular disorder, and diabetes, on the other hand, are generally identified as health risks for seniors with PWS.

Studies commissioned by U.S. Special Olympics point out that physicians, dentists and other health professionals are not receiving the training to adequately treat people with intellectual disabilities (Special Olympics, 2005). This, combined with the difficulties asso-ciated with communication for some individuals with PWS suggests that parents and caregivers need to be proactive about regular medical check-ups.

Medical problems. In a review of patients over age 30, Cassidy, Devi and Mukaida (1995), identified hypertension and diabetes as the major health problems of adulthood, with obesity, osteoporosis and restrictive lung disease also problematic.

At least 27 percent of the original sample studied by James (1987) died, between the ages of 17 and 46. The cause of death for the five who died beyond age 40 included two cases of pneumonia, one of kidney failure, and one from aspiration. Cause of death was not avail-able for the other individual. According to Eiholzer and Lee (2006), respiratory muscle weakness and the inability to compensate during acute lung disease may account for a "relatively high occurrence of pneumonia and fever-related mortality" (p. 122). Cor pulmonale (heart disease which follows from lung disease) is "the most common-ly reported cardiovascular complication in PWS and is often cited as a cause of mortality" (p. 128).

Most of the individuals in the present over-40 group reported stable health at the time of the interviews. Three have diabetes (two Type I and one Type II); two have arthritis (knees, ankle); four have scoliosis.   One man, previously requiring constant oxygen, now only carries it as a safety precaution on outings. One woman has asthma and a man has iron deficiency.

Hospitalizations. While the over-40 group as a whole was considered to be in good health, almost all had a history of earlier hospitalizations. It was reported that prior to supported independent living one woman had made regular visits to the wound clinic for skin care and was hospitalized almost annually for severe skin-picking. One woman had an earlier hospital admission for heart failure. Three had stays on a psychiatric ward.

Some of the over-40 group had been hospitalized in earlier years for surgeries: one man had three hernia operations (one inguinal, two hiatus); a woman had three knee surgeries; two women had gall bladder surgeries; a man had two intestinal by-pass operations; a woman had two surgeries to position rods in her back; and another required intervention for a pulmonary embolism. Surgical procedures after age 40 included a knee surgery and a hysterectomy.

One male had been to the Emergency Department on two occasions, once for water intoxication and then for severe abdominal pain; a woman had been to Emergency for severe cramps. One woman was taken to Emergency several times during the course of the present study. She was described as "very confused, withdrawn, lethargic and [with] loss of interest in food." She had "no standing nor sitting blood pressure and her heart rate dropped below 50." It was suspected that she was over-medicated so the mood stabilizer was withdrawn and she was more or less back to normal within five days.

Mental health

The National Advisory Council on Aging (NACA) report (2004) asserts that mental health problems for seniors with developmental disabilities tend to be attributed to the individual's disability, thus clouding the detection of problems that may be treatable. It goes on to say that differentiation between dementia, depression and syndrome-specific behaviours is especially challenging. This is exacerbated by the difficulty that a senior may have expressing personal problems.

Given the range of behaviours, the individual variability within PWS, and the high rate of speech and language difficulties associated with the syndrome, the identification of psychological problems within the aging PWS population may present a particular challenge. The NACA Report (2004) makes the point that there are few specialists with expertise in both developmental disability and psychogeriatrics. To find a specialist with an interest in aging and a knowledge of PWS is difficult.

In a British study (Boer et al., 2002) investigating the relation between genetic subtypes and psychiatric morbidity, 4 out of 5 subjects over the age of 40 who had a detailed psychiatric assessment had a clinical diagnosis, including: depressive psychosis, psychotic disorder, bipolar affective disorder, and mild depressive episode. All were on antipsychotic, mood stabilizer or antidepressant medication. Three had paranoid delusions.

Some individuals in the present study take daily prescription medications for behaviour and/or mental health concerns. One person takes 20 mg of Prozac and is less agitated and has no more tantrums. Twenty milligrams was ineffective for another – she requires 30 mg to effect change in her behaviours. One male has been on Wellbutrin for seven years. It has helped with anxiety reduction, weight loss and more appropriate eating behaviours. In contrast, a female who went on Wellbutrin lasted only three months because she became an "unbelievably impossible person." These examples underscore the variability in response to medications. Another woman has been on Haldol since age 19. Although alternatives have been tried they have all had negative consequences.

The personal stories of the individuals in this document affirm that response to medications is highly individual, and that adverse reactions do occur. Readers are referred to the Medic Alerts on the PWSA-USA website for further information on this topic.

Substance use

While adults with PWS may smoke and/or drink alcohol, there were no reported instances of this being problematic in the over-40 group.

Smoking. Waters et al. (2007) reported that only a small minority of adults with PWS in the U.K. are smokers (16.4%). Men were nearly five times more likely than women to smoke. Two of the 13 people profiled in the current document, both women, have been long-time tobacco smokers. One has been smoking for over 25 years; the other recently quit after smoking a half pack of cigarettes daily for more than 20 years.

Drinking. Some adults with PWS enjoy a social drink, including several in the present sample. Typically, drinking was described as "occasional" and "social." In younger years one man used to go for a lite beer once a month at the Legion with a worker, but there was no indication of regular drinking by anyone in the present group. One woman mentioned having a favourite drink, kahlua and milk, and another said she likes to be able to have a glass of wine with a meal in a restaurant on occasion.

Age of leaving home

With the exception of the two individuals who went into Michener Centre in Alberta (at ages 12 and 17), the individuals profiled in this document all moved from the family home as young adults. It should be noted that the oldest person left at the youngest age. She went into a provincial institution for the mentally handicapped, as was common in the day. The greatest number moved from the family residence in their twenties; the oldest left at age 30. In most cases moving out was a mutual decision; while discussion was initiated by the parent it was welcomed by the young adult. In the U.K., Waters et al. (2007) found the average age for entering into a care home was 20. The average age of leaving home for the present over-40 group was 25.7 years.

Residential options

Residential options vary within and across provinces, depending on the prevailing social services philosophy, eligibility criteria, and funding available within the region. It should be noted that PWS-specific group homes, long promoted as the best residential model by the PWSA-USA, only exist in one province in Canada. While parents may be attracted to this model, the sparsity of the PWS population in Canada has made group homes a viable option only in the more densely populated province of Ontario. An attempt in Vancouver in the mid-1980s lasted less than a year due to a lack of economic viability.

Two of the over-40 group, a female and a male from different provinces, had the experience of sharing accommodation with a peer with PWS earlier in their adult years. In both situations, however, the experience was short-lived due to issues of incompatibility. Both now enjoy supported independent living.

The Community Living Research Project (CLRP) in B.C. (2008) noted that "recent trends emphasizing inclusion and self-determination have resulted in a shift in residential activities reflecting choice, community living, and active participation" (p. 7) for adults with developmental disabilities. The authors cite home sharing and semi-independent living as two residential alternatives to group homes resulting from the shift. This shift is evident in the residential experiences of the individuals profiled in the current document as 75% had experienced group home living in their younger years, yet only 16.6 % remained in this model at the time of writing.

After reviewing the literature, the CLRP (2008) concluded that the residential options which promote quality of life share three important characteristics. They: "(1) resemble family homes, (2) are located in communities where individuals have a social network, and (3) have well-organized and directed levels of support" (p. 8).

All but two of the individuals profiled later in this book live in an urban context. Of those living in a rural environment, one lives on a small acreage in Alberta, and the other in a home on the outskirts of a small town on Vancouver Island. While there is quite a range in individual living situations, they can be grouped conveniently into three basic models: family living, group living and supported independent living.

Family living. The three people living with parents share some elements of their stories in common. In each situation they had lived away from home for a number of years. In two cases they were rescued by their parents because of health concerns. One had been married and living in another town; the other had lived unsuccessfully within the care system. In both cases they now live with a high degree of independence, as would occur with any other sibling returning to reside with a parent for a period of time as an adult. One shares the house, housekeeping and responsibilities for the animals with her mother. She hires her own support workers and determines her own program of activities. She stays on her own when her mother is away. The other has her own bedroom with television and computer. She borrows her parents' car to go to the mall or the Legion. She volunteers in the community without supervision. She stays on her own when her parents are away. In both of these examples there is more independence than is enjoyed by most in the supported independent living model described below. While they are good examples of supported independent living they are cited in this section because they reside in the home of a parent.

Group living. Three of the people live within a group living model. Again, each situation is slightly different:

- one woman lives in a private residence with caregivers and another lady with special needs

- one man lives in the home of his sister and brother-in-law along with three other residents with special needs
- one man lives in a PWS-specific group home along with five others with PWS.

The latter has lived in a PWS-specific group home for 12 years in Burlington. There are six such homes in Ontario. His mother recalls the "long and discouraging process" to get the first home established, but acknowledged the important contribution of the nutritionist whose program is still being followed more than 12 years later, and the psychologist who set up a reward program for both the home and the workshop.

There may be less independence with the group living model compared to the home living model described above. However, group living provides a safe environment with peer relationships which are not available in either of the other two models.

Supported independent living. Seven of the individuals in the over-40 group live within a supported independent living model. They all receive varying degrees of agency support. Each living situation has unique aspects:

- private apartment within an agency-operated building; night staff are on duty for the building and each unit is individually alarmed
- mobile home in a trailer park; the wall between the two smaller bedrooms was removed to create a second bedroom/office area for night staff
- house that is shared with another man with special needs; each has his own bedroom and the full use of the rest of the house; a third bedroom is for staff
- one bedroom unit in a small apartment building; night staff must set up a folding cot nightly
- bed-sitting room in the basement of the home of a care worker
- two-bedroom unit in a large apartment complex; the second bedroom is for staff
- three-bedroom townhouse which is shared with another man with special needs; the third bedroom is for staff.

There is considerable variation across the three residential models described. The use of a house, apartment, townhouse, mobile home and basement suite within the supported independent living model, for example, illustrate the adaptation to the local housing market conditions. There has been a shift in recent years to support more independent living in the community. Group living models, while still an option in most areas, do not have the same degree of popularity as in the past. At best, the family living model must be considered temporary. As most children outlive their parents there is usually a point at which the adult with special needs must move into an alternative model.

It is interesting to note that only three individuals (23%) were living with parents in this study. By contrast, 48 % of those over age 40 in the U.K. study by Waters et al. (2007) were living at home with their family. While 54 % of the over-40 group were supported in independent living in Canada, only 1.6 % of the total U.K. adult PWS population experienced the same opportunity.

Employment

The Community Living Research Project (2008), examined employment incentives and policies for persons with disabilities across the provinces and other industrialized countries and found that flexible employment supports and creative income assistance policies make it possible for people with significant disabilities to maximize labour market participation. Highlighting the legislation and policies of the five western provinces, they point out that while provinces have a similar medical model to determine eligibility, they vary considerably in their benefits, asset limits and earning exemptions policies. From the client perspective, they suggest that "the prospect of losing benefits can act as a strong disincentive to seeking employment income" (p. 19). From the employer perspective, the "competition among agencies for clients who are easier rather than harder to serve" (p. 1) can be another disincentive. Clients who require more one-on-one supervision, as is required in job coaching, are more costly to support. For-profit agencies, in particular, may place higher value on the economic bottom line rather than promoting the employment interests of the clients.

To what extent do seniors with PWS participate in the labour market? At the time of interviews, no one in the current sample experienced regular remunerative employment. However, not everyone was happy with the lack of employment options. One man, for example, lamented his lack of opportunity to have a real job, like his friends. Others, having had various work experiences, once had expectations or ambitions to work, but had resigned themselves to the reality of non-remunerative activities. One woman has since acquired a regular weekly paper route. Her worker drives her to the route and observes from her vehicle. Others make pocket money by selling their crafts, providing a service such as dog-walking, or earning incentives while doing contract work at their workshop.

Day activities

Nugent (2007) points out that employment will be too anxiety provoking for some people with PWS. She asserts that "better options for them will be sheltered employment or a roster of well chosen daily activities" and that "the priority is choosing day program options that maintain the physical and mental health of the individual" (p. 77). Day activities of the over-40 group vary but essentially fall into three categories: workshop or group programs (38%), individualized day programs (46%), and retirement (15%).

Sheltered workshops/group day programs. Traditionally, workshops and day programs operate from established facilities. In these settings attendees may have choices and be able to individualize their activities within the limits of what the programs offer. Some programs have a vocational focus. Two of the group, in different provinces, enjoy working on contract jobs from the community arranged through their workshops. Other workshop attendees enjoy doing crafts, latch-hooking, and making jewelry and cards. One of the men, on the other hand, reports to the day program but chooses activities that take him out into the community. He has enjoyed participating with an on-air radio program at the local university, showing animals in a shopping mall and helping in a soup kitchen.

Individual day programs. More recently, individualized day programs have evolved to better meet personal needs. They often bridge the residential, vocational and social-recreational domains. They all have flexibility to address individual circumstances and utilize community resources.

Some individualized programs have more of a vocational focus. One man's program involves volunteer work, largely for schools and churches. A woman volunteers with non-profit agencies, doing computer data entry, photocopying, collating, and envelope stuffing. As a trained clown, "Blossom" occasionally volunteers to spread cheer at hospitals. Another woman spends one day each week at Indefinite Arts where she likes to do ceramics and painting. Some of her work has sold, giving her a 70% commission.

Independent living is supported through many day program activities, for example: menu planning, grocery shopping, meal preparation, and budgeting. Almost all individualized programs have an exercise component. Some walk, swim, dance, bowl or go to the gym with their workers.

Individualized programs are flexible and can take advantage of community events, allowing people to take in touring performances and special holiday or seasonal celebrations. One woman even attended a couple of political rallies and was able to expound on the issues of concern.

Retirement. Those who fall into the retirement category are quite self-directed in their activities. They experience some health limitations and pursue more sedentary activities. One woman, for example, enjoys her computer, the Ladies Auxiliary at the Legion and her volunteer activities, all of which she does without the presence of a support worker; a man enjoys his collections, church involvement and going for coffee. He is still accompanied by a worker but his activities have changed from a vocational to a social-recreational focus.

Socialization

Individuals with PWS are often portrayed as deficient in social skills and adaptive behaviours. Early literature described: poor social skills (Leconte, 1981); social isolation due to poor interactions, inability to pick up social cues, immaturity, and the need for control (Cassidy, 1984); impulsivity and poor social judgment (Mitchell, 1988); and difficulty in developing friendships (Levine & Wharton, 1993). Most of these descriptors were applied to a young PWS population. What can be said about the social skills of older adults with PWS?

Integrated adult interactions. Individuals from the over-40 group were only observed by the author in the context of small group situations involving family and care workers. All were friendly, polite and socially appropriate. With one exception, they were able to answer questions relating to personal information. Most were able to describe experiences and tell stories with detail and expression.

Some parents and caregivers described characteristics which they considered to be problematic in adult social interactions, including: perseveration on a topic, interrupting or "butting in" to the conversation of others, introducing a new topic inappropriately, dominating the conversation, talking loudly or excitedly, and invading personal space. While these were cited as problematic behaviours inhibiting socialization, they did not necessarily occur all of the time nor were they shared by all.

Peer interactions. Members of the over-40 group identified a range of peer social interactions. For example, one man enjoys going for coffee with a special friend, a woman visits with a girl-friend in a suite downstairs, and another enjoys sharing music and movies with friends. One likes to go to dances to be with friends and another says that she has friends at her program. One man and his fiancée like to socialize with friends, and another man likes the contact with people through his church. For another man, moving into a PWS-specific group home had social benefits. "At last he was a member of a group after having felt alone for so long," said his mother. The youngest woman enjoys integrated social activities. She bowls and clogs with non-handicapped peers and enjoys going to the Legion. Several enjoy structured group activities through special needs groups such as Special Olympics, Therapeutic Riding or the local Association for Community Living. Siblings for one individual acknowledged that while peer social supports had been there in earlier years, their sister is now in need of more social contacts.

In contrast to group home living, which often has structured group activities, the home or independent living models allow for a more natural level of social activity. Within the over-40 group, people plan their activities in advance and mark them on their calendars. During the week they generally enjoy staying at home and watching television or movies in the evenings and retire early as they must get up early the next morning to go to their work or day program.

While no data were collected on the quality of peer social interactions, the fact that nobody with PWS complained about a lack of peer social activities or friendships, and no parents or guardians identified peer socialization as an area of concern, suggests considerable satisfaction with this domain. In some cases, however, there were concerns cited by agency staff about social skills deficits, for example, invading personal space or the lack of conversational skills. Some individuals require continued social skill support, even as seniors.

Independent activities. Some preferred activities for members of the over-40 group do not include social interactions. Doing jigsaw puzzles and word searches are basically solitary activities. Watching television, particularly in independent living, is usually done alone. Beyond the learning stage, unless part of a structured program, crafts done in the home such as knitting, crocheting or rug-hooking are also independent activities. Everyone seems to have some hobby, or some preferred activities, which are not social in nature.

Psycho-sexual interests. Half of the individuals over 40 have a special on-going relationship with a member of the opposite sex that is very important to them. Two individuals, one female and one male, are engaged to be married to peers who were met through their day programs or social activities. Rings have been given and were proudly displayed. One mother suggested, however, that her daughter might have a "perpetual engagement."

One woman has been married and divorced. She has also lived with another partner. At least three of the group have had sexual relations. Two women have been in relationships which they acknowledge were abusive. Abuse is a topic of concern for parents, regardless of the age of their child.

Transportation

Individuals with PWS must get to and from their workshop or place of activity, and get about the community for their individualized day programs and leisure activities. Whether residing in a rural or urban setting, transportation is a major consideration. Difficulties particularly arise when adults with PWS want to initiate evening or weekend activities that require transportation.

Family and friends. It is awkward to always have to rely on family or friends for transportation. One woman explained that she might like to take in more church activities or visit her mother more often, but said that she felt awkward about asking family or friends for rides. Siblings already routinely pick her up to go to church on Sunday.

Public transit. One man uses public transit when he and his fiancée want to get from the suburbs into Victoria for special activities. He must account for all monies that he spends and stick to a pre-discussed schedule.

Care workers. Care workers usually provide transportation in their personal vehicles to facilitate individualized day program activities for PWS clients. A vehicle is usually a requirement of the job. Because it is their personal vehicle there are occasions when the line between work and personal activity becomes blurred.

One woman, for example, complained when a care worker did personal errands, bought groceries and stopped for junk food while paid to be providing service. Transportation is essential for the success of individualized day programs, but the lack of supervision of the care worker leaves travel time open to possible mis-use.

Special needs bus. In some communities, special needs vans or small busses operated by local associations transport children and adults with special needs to and from school and day programs. One woman in the over-40 group gets picked up at home and returned after her day at a workshop. The door-to-door service is appreciated by the family as it minimizes the opportunities for things to go wrong en route.

Driver's license. Some adults with PWS want to learn to drive. Should they be allowed? Parents express concerns about the potential for poor judgment and impulsivity when driving. They also fear the implications of freedom and independence on food acquisition.

According to the PWSA(UK) web site, a few people with PWS in the U.K. have had driving lessons, but they gave up when they found it too difficult. The site mentions awareness of one person in the U.K. who holds a full licence, and mentions that at least one case is known in the U.S.A.

One person in the current group holds a driver's license. She has been driving in B.C. for 25 years. In this period she has had only one ticket for a speed violation in a school zone. While living in another town she would drive three hours to visit her parents. Now in her forties, she doesn't drive as much as she used to. She drives to the mall or to the Legion. She explained that she pre-plans her routes carefully and carries a cell phone, and if she gets nervous she pulls over to the side of the road.

Agency care

While there may not be agencies experienced with PWS in all communities, there are at least some agencies in each province that have acquired knowledge and experience working with this syndrome.

Agency experience. Collectively there is a lot of expertise that can be a resource to families and other agencies. The SKILLS Society in Edmonton has 20 years of experience; the SCOPE Society and Rehoboth, in Calgary, have worked with individuals with PWS for more than a decade. In Burlington, Headon House and

ARC Industries have more than 12 years experience. The Hearthstone
Community Group in Selkirk has 14 years experience. This list is
illustrative of long-term stable agencies across the country providing
services to adults with PWS.

Waiting lists. Waiting lists are a reality in many locales, particularly when in transition from youth to adult services, or when
changing communities as an adult. One woman who moved to
Victoria in her early thirties had to wait two years before getting into
a workshop program. Delays in service can occur for other reasons as
well. At the time of writing, a woman in Calgary, is without support
because the agency is having difficulty recruiting and maintaining
support workers.

Secular versus religious agencies. Families of faith have been
able to acquire day program and residential services provided by religious organizations for their family member. Organizations such
as St. Vincent de Paul, L'Arche, Rehoboth, and Communitas provide
services as a call to ministry to serve the needs of individuals with
developmental disabilities. Those preferring secular agencies have
chosen both for-profit (private contractors) and not-for-profit agencies (e.g., Associations for Community Living). In general, not-for-profit
agencies, whether secular or religious, seem to offer more stable, long-
term service.

Agency interests. Some parents and individuals with PWS
have experienced disappointments with the services received from
some agencies. One mother described how, when her son moved into
a new group home, she was not allowed to have contact with him for
one month. She felt that this was "not natural" and it was "like being
penalized." This was a policy of the agency, ostensibly to facilitate
client adjustment. Or was it to make their management tasks easier?
Another parent was critical of agency employees who would not listen
to either her or her daughter about what management techniques they
had found to work. This criticism has been echoed by many parents
in other age groups as well.

Despite policies which promote a client-centred approach,
programs do not always serve the "best" interests of a client. Worker
characteristics and demands of the job may give way to such reali-
ties as schedule convenience, staff complacency, or personal comfort.
One parent complained that agency workers did not follow through
with team goals; another that the diet requirements were not followed;

another that the staff did not respect the personal space of the individual. A lack of supervision resulted in sexual abuse in one instance. One mother, concerned that her daughter was not happy with some of the workshop activities, feared the consequences if she complained and felt that she just needed to be thankful for the service received.

On the other hand, there is testimony about agency employees who have gone the extra mile and agencies that have provided reliable long-term service. The criticism of agencies underscores the need for parents and guardians to explore agency policies and procedures when considering a placement. When shopping for services the onus is on the parent/guardian to exercise due diligence beforehand and then to remain vigilant.

3

Aging with PWS: Some quality of life considerations

B rown and Brown (2003) present a comprehensive framework for understanding key ideas and principles involved in a quality of life approach to working with individuals with disabilities. Believing that all humans are entitled to enjoy quality lives, they formulate eight principles which emphasize personal meaning, value, enjoyment and happiness of life. They assert that a quality of life approach:

- focuses most on what is important to the individual
- supports action that increases personal satisfaction and decreases dissatisfaction
- stresses that opportunities to improve must be within the individual's grasp
- insists that personal choice should be exercised, whenever possible, in selecting opportunities
- improves the person's self-image
- increases levels of personal empowerment
- considers lifespan implications, and
- recognizes inter-and intra-individual variability (p. 108).

These principles can be used as a quick checklist to assess how successful particular supports and services are in promoting an individual's quality of life. They should be kept in mind while reading this section.

The following discussion of quality of life is based on thematic analysis of open-ended responses to quality of life key words and questions provided by individuals with PWS and their parents/

caregivers. It also includes in-home observations by the writer. It places a high value on the perceptions of those most knowledgeable and experienced with PWS. The following topics are not exhaustive, rather they are a beginning for the focus of discussion on quality of life and persons aging with PWS.

Quality of care

Individuals with PWS, and their parents/caregivers, identified a number of factors which contribute to their understanding of quality of care

Staff characteristics. Adults with PWS know when they are being well-served by staff. They have complimented workers for: understanding PWS, helping with problems, speaking slowly to help understanding, being fun to be with, going for walks, taking them on trips, sharing family experiences, and having a sense of humour. They also recognize when they are not being well-supported. They have criticized workers for: lack of personal supervision, lack of control of other residents, not enforcing diet restrictions, and not listening.

Parents, too, have commented on the seeming lack of commitment of staff. They have been critical of the: high rate of turn-over, unwillingness to learn from the file history, lack of rapport with the adult under care, lack of rapport with the parent, and an authoritarian attitude.

Some workers, particularly those of faith-based agencies, may have a sense of "calling" to human services work. To follow the calling is as important as the economic benefits received from the job. They are more likely to be long-term service providers.

Continuity of care. Continuity is a factor in quality of care. Competitive employment opportunities, particularly in times of booming economies, create a high turn-over rate in the human services field. There were several stories of dissatisfaction with short-term personnel. A recent newspaper article describes the impact of losing a worker on Margaret, profiled in the next section (Cryderman, 2008). "Near tears...Tyler...said her sister is supposed to receive round-the-clock care, but the agency that helps her doesn't have enough staff." The problem started when a worker who provided care four days a week left the demanding job to go to work at a grocery chain store for $1.50 an hour more. In labour-hungry Calgary $15 per hour is not enough to attract and retain qualified workers, but it is all that government funding will provide. The lack of continuity left Margaret and those responsible for her care in crisis. This was not an isolated situation. Over an eight month period, three out of four caregivers had left the team.

The transience of staff is sometimes a difficult item to address. One young college-trained human services worker explained that workers can make better money working in the fast food industry in Alberta than in providing personal care. She saw the signing bonus offered by some fast food outlets as an attraction, and considered a regular job with fast foods to have less responsibility and stress. Yet she chose to remain in her individual support role because she had grown close to her client and family. Working with a Christian service organization, she derived considerable satisfaction from her work. Continuity of care is frequently linked to money issues, whether staff financial needs or agency funding.

Knowledge of PWS. Workers and agencies vary in their knowledge of PWS. Some are more willing than others to learn. Some agencies provide in-service training, including attendance at conferences, job shadowing and literature to read. David's mother wanted to make the point that knowledgeable resource people, a nutritionist and a psychologist experienced with PWS, were brought in to assist with staff training when Headon House was established. Their expertise was important to the establishment of home routines and management practices.

Most parents agree that PWS syndrome-specific knowledge is essential to understanding and working with the syndrome. Ironically, the expertise of parents is not always received well by agencies.

Application of policies. Agencies are expected to have policies which fall in line with provincial legislation and social services ministry guidelines. Policies, however, may be subject to interpretation. Individual workers may exercise a rigid approach, or allow more latitude in order to meet individual circumstances. Most parents want greater flexibility and more creative solutions to their problems. They decry the rigidity of government bureaucracies; they are also critical of agency staff who are similarly unaccommodating.

Two policy areas were most commonly cited as problematic by parents:

- *food access controls* - some agencies have been unwilling to lock up food or restrict kitchen access (arguing that this violates client rights)

- *restrictive procedures* - agencies vary in their willingness to apply restrictive procedures (eg., taped gloves to discourage skin picking, locked doors to prevent night walking).

Parents are adamant that quality care requires clear policies which realistically address the needs of adults with PWS.

Parent involvement. Parents appreciate it when their experience and expertise are acknowledged and their in-put welcomed. They have reported being offended when asked to stay away from their child's place of residence, or when they are not included as a member of the team in decision making. Often agency workers have minimal, if any, experience with PWS. They must recognize that parents are the real experts - they have intimate knowledge of, and years of experience with, their child. Workers need to recognize this resource and take advantage of it. Unfortunately, some parents may seem to be overly aggressive at times, causing agency staff to withdraw to a defensive position or to avoid contact.

PWS voice. Angela, a strong self-advocate, who interviews and hires her own staff with her individualized funding, has prepared two hand-outs, with the help of her mother, for her staff. The first one deals with "Prader-Willi syndrome misconceptions," where she explains 11 misconceptions and how they relate to her. The second is titled "How to support me." In her words, "some just don't get-it, so I want to make it very clear, the ways I need your support!" (Kinash, 2007).

During a staffing conflict, Angela identified the following issues that she had with a worker:

- offering to share food beyond what her diet allowed
- eating foods with lingering after-smells (e.g., chewing strongly scented bubble gum; eating Caesar salad for lunch)
- stopping daily for coffee (and power bar, granola bar or other snack item) while she waited in the car
- doing personal food shopping on work time.

Despite the literature that had been provided, the worker did not take seriously that she was working for the client and that she was expected to follow a plan that minimized food distractions for her. Care is not something that is simply designed by others with professional wisdom; quality care must take into consideration the voice of those with PWS.

In one situation, the PWS voice could not be freely heard. An individual was placed in a provincial institution for the mentally handicapped as a teen, thereby coming under the care of the Public Guardian. Despite now living in community and enjoying new freedoms, his story could not be told without the scrutiny and consent of the Public Guardian's office. While others of comparable intellect are able to speak for themselves, this individual was really not free to make his own decisions because of circumstances and a parent decision that was made 25 years earlier. A worker from the Office of the Public Guardian is responsible for protecting his best interests, including overseeing the quality of care received.

In most situations there was a healthy appreciation for the PWS voice by parents and caregivers. Generally, parents encouraged personal planning and decision making. Independent living and individualized program planning similarly encourage and support PWS voice.

Economic circumstances. Uncertainty with respect to long-term planning detracts from quality care. Parents all have questions: Will there be cut-backs to programs and services this year? Will government funding allow for a cost-of-living increase for staff? Will there be more than a one-year funding commitment?... and so on. In the eyes of parents, quality care is directly related to the stability of government funding. Economic uncertainty makes it difficult for agencies and private contractors to plan.

All of the adults in the over-40 group were receiving a disability income from their provincial government. The rates vary across provinces. Because budgets use finite numbers, it is difficult to obtain funds for a new program or service if they have not been planned well in advance and contained in budget proposals.

Some parents have established trusts to ensure long-term security for the adult with PWS. Funds held in trust are not treated as an asset of the person with a disability and thus do not disqualify them from receiving assistance. Funds can be used for approved expenditures to a set limit annually. They can supplement and enhance the quality of the care, for example, by covering medical or health-related aids and supplies, or caregiving and home support costs.

Independence and choice making

Independence, as explained by most of the adults interviewed, has two important aspects, freedom from parental supervision and the opportunity to have choices and make decisions about one's life. Thus living away from the parents' home and receiving 24/7 attendant care is considered to be "independent living." Once freed from the intense level of supervision, often abhorred as a teen, and supported to make personal decisions about day-to-day living, even residing in a group home can meet the definition of independence. This does not mean to say that choices and decision making cannot occur in the context of the family home. Each of the adults living with family were treated respectfully and encouraged to make their own decisions. For example, there was tolerance of one person who chose to smoke, although she was asked to do it outside; another was allowed to borrow the car on occasion; a third was able to plan social activities requiring the use of public transit.

Individualized day programming, like independent living, optimizes personal choice making. For example, whether choosing activities, setting schedules for work activity, or choosing leisure and recreation activities, there is the need to express personal preferences. Individualized programming is committed to empowering individual choice making. Without some degree of independence and choice making there can be little sense of self-control and self-worth.

With an out-of-home placement for their son or daughter, almost all parents report an improvement in relations with their child and a reduction in personal stress. While adults with PWS do not express it in the same terms, their actions suggest that they value their new status. For example, they come home to visit as their schedules permit. As one mother explained, "he comes home on the weekend to visit, *if* he doesn't have anything else on." In other words, her son is setting his own priorities and making his own decisions.

Residential supports

More time is spent in the residential environment than in any other setting. The supports available in the residential situation contribute importantly to quality of life.

Effective residential supports. Feedback from the over-40 group identified a number of elements related to their residential situations that were viewed positively:

- *contact with family* - either living in close proximity to enable visits, or regular contact by telephone
- *access to community* - being able to participate in social, recreational and leisure experiences of choice

- *personal space* - being able to self-determine how to decorate and utilize living areas
- *independence* - being able to determine a personal schedule and exercise choice of activities
- *possessions* - being able to select and own home furnishings and display collections.

Generally, they expressed satisfaction with their personal circumstances. No one was asking for, or in need of, a different residential placement.

Ineffective residential supports. There were two important areas, however, identified as concerns:

- *transportation* - having to rely on care workers for transportation; and having to ask friends and family for rides to activities in the evening or on weekends
- *staff changes* - having to adjust to new faces and relationships because of staff turn-over.

Both of these areas create uncertainties. They are situations over which adults with PWS have no sense of control.

While not identified by individuals with PWS, it was evident during home visits that the personality and commitment of individual support workers was a very important aspect of residential support. Similarly, it was the personalities of parents and family members that enabled those who were living in home situations to be successful.

Best and worst things in life

In identifying the "best" things about their lives, the most frequent comments had to do with living status. "I can be independent downstairs," said a woman living in a basement suite. "I can watch T.V. in my own area," she explained. After years of group living experiences she valued her privacy. Another identified "living in my own apartment" and "having the opportunity to do things in the community." Her supported independent living model encouraged personal choice making and community involvement. "I have a good life," she said. Another woman, living in her own apartment with the same model of 24/7 support identified "living on my own" as the best thing in her life. Supporting her boyfriend through a period of recovery while in the hospital was also a recent highlight.

The most senior of the group, with many years of supported independent living, simply identified "when things are going well," reflecting her satisfaction with her present lifestyle. The worst thing in life for her was "when things were different and it was a hard struggle," referring to earlier group living experiences. The one having experienced the greatest of independence of any in the group found the computer to be the best thing in her life. Now living a less active, "retired" lifestyle in a rural setting, she valued her computer, particularly for email, Facebook and games. She is very competent with the computer and uses it daily. And for a male who is engaged to be married, it is not surprising that the relationship with his fiancée is the best thing in his life.

It took more reflection to name the "worst" things about their lives. In fact, only 3 (23%) identified any negatives in their lives. For a woman, whose volunteer work schedule varies daily, "days when I do not have work" was the worst thing. She asserted that she likes to be kept busy. For a woman having experienced abuse from a partner, "wife abuse" was identified. She also admitted that "not learning by my experiences" and "people controlling me" were part of worst case situations for her. For another woman who has difficulty walking and must use a walking cane, it was the coming winter, when it would be slippery, that was cited as a negative in her life.

Greatest accomplishments

When asked "Of what accomplishments are you most proud?" the range of responses fell into several themes. In some cases the reflections were of a long-term nature, in others they were more concerned with the present. At other times during the interview individuals described things that they felt good about, successes that they had experienced, things that they had done, or places that they had been, yet didn't identify them as accomplishments per se:

- *relationships* - Two of the group were engaged and spoke proudly of their relationships. Others spoke fondly of their girlfriend or boyfriend. One woman cited "people who understand me" as important.
- *residence* - One woman cited living independently with support as her major accomplishment. Indeed, it has taken her almost 20 years to gain this degree of independence. After 25 years in an institution, a man feels good about finally living in the community. Understanding that it took him almost 15 years to achieve community-based living

there is more of an appreciation for this as an accomplishment. Everyone else felt good about their current place of residence, although not everyone cited it as an accomplishment.

- *recognitions* - For some, public recognition was seen as an accomplishment. One woman proudly shared a copy of a newsletter in which she was featured as "Blossom" the clown. Another told about winning a ribbon at the Calgary Stampede for her rug-hooking entry. John, whose autobiography appears at the end of this document, was recognized by the Ontario Association of Community Living for his work in self-advocacy and the People First organization.

- *achievements* - One individual spoke about specific achievements, like graduating from school and taking a course. Another cited her collections as a source of pride. No longer requiring oxygen, and weight loss, were achievements for another. Having a driver's license, while not self-identified as an achievement, is certainly an accomplishment that few with PWS have achieved.

- *activities* - One woman had an altruistic response, citing "the things that I can do in the community help others" as a source of pride. Another also said that she was proud of activities that she can do in the community. Her individualized program has allowed her to follow her interests, including cultural events, physical activities and even participating in a political protest. For a woman who spent 12 years in Michener Centre, participation in such activities is an accomplishment. Some spoke of, or showed photos of, special vacations that they had taken. Again, they felt good about their participation in these special events while not necessarily identifying them as accomplishments. One was particularly proud of participation in her sister's wedding party. From the perspective of the caregivers, successful international travel, cruises and all-inclusive vacations were definite accomplishments.

Accomplishments can take many forms. The themes cited reflect the normalcy of accomplishments, reminding readers that all can achieve, albeit at different levels, and that all can enjoy the success of their accomplishments.

Relationships

When asked to identify their friends, the responses of this over-40 group fell into three categories: paid staff, peers and boy/girl friends.

Paid staff. When living in a group home or supported independent living there are always staff present. Staff supervise outings, whether it be an individual night at the movies or a games night for all residents. In the absence of the opportunity to develop peer friendships it is understandable why trusted staff are viewed as friends. One individual listed four staff and one peer as friends. Another named her favourite worker and a member of the worker's family as friends. Another identified her day worker, who had been with her for more than five years. One identified her music teacher, a constant in her life for several years. And another named a respite worker from many years earlier, describing her as "my second mom." Despite the fact that they now lived in different cities, she remained important in her life.

While it might be argued that paid staff are transient, in some cases they may not be as transient as peers. It is the trusted relationship over the long term that gives them the status of friends.

Peers. One woman likes to go for walks with a friend from her bowling team. Another visits a friend in her apartment building where she enjoys music, videos, nail painting and having coffee. Others identified peers from a workshop program or a leisure activity as friends, although they never spend time together outside of that context.

There is a noticeable absence of friendships with non-handicapped peers. However, given the structured lifestyles and high degree of supervision that most have, there is little opportunity to meet such peers. There were a few examples of casual friendships as a result of integrated leisure activities, but no non-handicapped peers were named when asked to identify friends.

Boyfriends and girlfriends. As indicated earlier, half of the individuals over age 40 had a special on-going relationship with a member of the opposite sex that was very important to them. One man was described as being very social and having many friends. He enjoys spending most time, however, with his fiancée. A woman who is engaged speaks fondly of time with her fiancé as well. Another man is also described as being very social. "A lot of people seem to know him," says his mother. He enjoys spending time with females. One woman has a male friend who she sees at dances and who comes to supper on occasion. Another woman was hurting from a relationship that had been terminated because of parental concern for her safety.

Apart from the last story of a broken relationship, nobody raised a concern about the nature of, or a lack of, friendships, including individuals with PWS, their parents or service providers. Most individuals within this over-40 group have adequate social skills to make and maintain friends according to their need.

Possessions

In order to receive disability benefits from the government there are limits placed on the amount of money that a person with disabilities can have in his or her bank account. As a result, guardians do a good job ensuring that income is appropriately expended in support of the person with PWS.

In visits to 10 out of the 13 residences it was observed that all individuals enjoyed much more than basic necessities. For example, everyone had a television, and most a CD and/or DVD player. Three had their own computers. And everyone had sufficient disposable income to enjoy:
- building their collections
- pursuing their hobbies
- participating in leisure – recreation activities
- taking vacations.

Living spaces were well-maintained and decorated according to individual taste with: pictures, posters, puzzles, photographs and awards. Feedback from parents/guardians suggested that everyone gets what they need, and in most cases what they want.

Disposable income was often spent on collectibles. Some bought new items such as videos, CDs and DVDs and amassed large collections. Others collected second-hand items such as old purses and used coffee mugs. While the latter were a cheaper investment, they still contributed to the same problem, a lack of space for display or storage. In a few cases the size of collections had to be limited.

Finding appropriate clothing for individuals who are short and heavy can be a problem. It takes more effort, and cost to try to be stylish. Those who had lost significant amounts of weight appreciated the opportunity to "buy off the rack" and they were proud of their clothes.

Some individuals in independent living have purchased pets or animals. For example, one has a pair of finches and another has dogs, cats and a pair of llamas. One man had a puppy for a short period of time but its care was too much for him. At the time of writing he was looking for a more mature dog that would be easier to manage.

Recreation – leisure

In general, those over age 40 are quite active with a balance of solitary and social activities. While two individuals participate in more sedentary activities due to health limitations, the rest remain physically active. As can be seen in Figure 2, the recreation and leisure activities list contains some high energy activities. Everyone identified some gross motor activities which they did on a weekly basis, although some varied with the seasons. All included some sedentary activities. The two most popular sedentary activities were watching television and listening to music. The two most popular physical activities were walking and swimming. Some of the sedentary activities were things that could be done conveniently while watching television. Three needed to have their hands occupied with a craft in order to reduce the likelihood of skin-picking while watching television.

Figure 2
Recreation - leisure activities

amusement parks	Guys' Night Out
bingo	gym circuits
board games	hiking
bowling	Internet use
cards	jig-saw puzzles
church	listening to music
clogging	watching movies
collections	needlepoint
computer games	paint-by-numbers
crafts	playing an instrument
crocheting	public speaking
cross-stitch	rug-hooking
crosswords	shopping
curling	sidoku
dog-walking	swimming
educational games	singing
fill-in word puzzles	television
Game Boy	upgrading courses
games night	visiting friends
garage sales	walking
going for coffee	word searches

Individuals who were higher functioning were more likely to engage in language and number-based activities such as crossword puzzles, word searches, sidoku, and computer or Internet use.

Craft activities, knitting, crocheting, needlepoint and rug-hooking were done exclusively by females. Board games and card games were identified exclusively by males. Participation in Games Night and Guys' Night Out were also male activities.

While activities sponsored by Special Olympics and the Community Living Associations are popular, some integrated community recreation activities have been accessed as well (e.g., dance classes, music lessons, gym memberships).

Physical activity has become a lifetime discipline for everyone. Even after three knee surgeries, which make walking difficult, one woman rides a stationary bike daily, enjoys swimming and bowling with Special Olympics, and horseback riding with a therapeutic riding association. Even with rods in her back, leg braces and crutches, the oldest member of the group has daily exercise built into her individual day program, such as going to the gym, shopping, and dog-walking.

Nobody related any stories about a lack of access to recreation-leisure activities or socially discriminatory practices. While this does not mean to say that there have not been any in the past, it does suggest that there were none of significance in recent memory.

Church

The opportunity to practice their faith, a faith that they were raised with, is important to some individuals with PWS. For some it means being able to attend church; for others it includes serving in the church. One man has continued to attend church with his parents for the last ten years since moving from the family home. His faith is an important part of his life. He participates in daily devotions and says grace at mealtimes. He has served as an usher and volunteers to help at coffee time. In another province a man goes to church with his worker. He similarly serves as an usher. He has a good relationship with a former pastor who confirmed him 30 years ago and who takes him out for coffee each month.

One woman used to attend church with her mother, but now that her mother no longer drives she does not have the opportunity. In reflection, she said that she particularly enjoyed singing hymns. Another woman professed a personal faith, explaining that she prays a lot. She does not attend church, although the residential agency staff asserted that the opportunity was there if she wanted it.

One woman goes to church weekly with one of her siblings who provides the transportation. She sees her mother at church and visits with her most Sundays. Church provided her with a wide network of social contacts in the past, particularly when she participated in Faith and Light.   Today there is not the same level of social connectedness. A man attends church regularly, always sitting with his godmother.

Many of the same behavioural issues exist in church settings as they do in the home and elsewhere in the community. There are reports of falling asleep during prayers and difficulties with community pot-lucks and buffets. But these are heavily outweighed by the expressions of support which comes from the church community.

Faith is a personal experience. It is hard to know how important it is in the quality of life of people who may have difficulty expressing themselves. In the tribute to Ray, a man with PWS who died at age 52, a friend wrote that "he who lived so much of his last years in silence, could all at once burst out singing along a gospel song on a tape in my car" (Jamin, 1990). Such spontaneous song, was surely a testimony to the importance of the gospel music in this man's life. For some, the rituals of their faith, such as prayer and church attendance, are vitally important. They choose to participate in church-related activities because they add to their quality of life.

Vacations

The opportunity to take an annual vacation, or save toward a major trip, is something that most Canadian families enjoy. Most members of the over-40 group take vacations, either with family, with an agency or through independent travel with support.

Family vacations. One woman attended almost every PWSA-USA annual conference with her parents up until the passing of her father a few years ago. This was an annual vacation that took her away from her daily routines and out of the country. One of the men had trips to the west coast of Vancouver Island and Hawaii in recent years with his parents. Another woman went on a three day cruise and four days at Disneyworld with her sister.

Agency travel. Others have the opportunity to travel with an agency. One lady has taken several major trips over the years. When living with L'Arche she travelled to Japan and Korea. Under her present agency she has made trips to Disneyland and Disneyworld.

One of the men has made two major trips, while in his forties, to compete at the Special Olympics National Games in Charlottetown (2004) and Quebec City (2008). While the purpose of the travel was competition, a break from daily routines and the opportunity to experience a new location and do some sightseeing made this like a vacation.

Independent travel. At 38, one woman took her first independent vacation when she planned for and travelled to Vancouver Island, accompanied by her worker. Another woman travelled independently by international air travel to visit her parents when she was younger. While individualized planning offers more flexibility for personal travel, it is difficult to facilitate if 24/7 care is required.

While travel opportunities and vacations may not happen annually, they do happen for some, even after age 40. The enthusiasm with which individuals share their photo albums and memorabilia is testimony to the contribution of travel and vacations to their quality of life.

Unmet wants and needs

At age 40, John wrote about a want similar to that expressed by others with PWS - "I want to have the CHOICE to decide what I want in my life." He went on to say, "I have the right to have the same CHOICES in life that you do. Without choices my right to freedom is being denied." Without such freedoms there is a diminished quality of life.

Issues centred on staffing can be a significant unmet need. Requiring 24/7 support to live independently, one woman's agency was unable to find a replacement when a worker quit to take a higher paying job, leaving her without many hours of coverage. This left her sister and brother-in-law, both working full-time, to try to provide the missing support. Another profound staffing need was expressed when one woman said "I need workers who understand what torments my brain." Clearly qualified staffing is a need, a critical need if the independent living model is to be successful.

One man expressed that he would love to be working at a "real" job. He even knew where he would like to work – in a pet store or bussing tables at Starbucks. He wanted to work at a real job "like some of my friends." Clearly this was an unmet want that could enhance his quality of life. His desire for such a job was not considered unreasonable by those closest to him. It was not unreasonable based on the experiences of others as well. In another province, a man did a similar job, bussing tables in a restaurant, even though it was only twice weekly. This was his job, and he did it for 12 years.

Another woman, who passed away at age 45, had also bussed tables daily in a restaurant for seven years.

Not all unmet wants are quite so difficult to meet. One of the ladies expressed the desire for a relatively small item. She wanted a larger table so that she could more effectively do her crafts while sitting in front of her television. With this convenience she thought that her evening leisure would be more enjoyable.

Best and worst aspects of growing older

Health and end-of-life issues were prominent "worst" aspects of growing older. One woman admitted that words didn't come as easily now and she is more forgetful. She recognized these as a sign of aging and indicated concern. Another woman who has experienced many hospitalizations over the years spoke of her medical history and explained about some recurring pains and developing arthritis. Another woman feared "ending up in hospital, being bed-ridden, with no company." Similarly, another feared "not having someone with me when I am in need" and "facing death alone."

On the positive side one woman explained that "getting smarter" and "learning by one's mistakes" were good aspects of aging. The youngest of the group identified "being an adult" as important to her. At the age of 40 she felt that she had only recently attained independent adult status. Still recovering from a broken relationship, she added "learning what love is all about" as a positive. The oldest member of the group felt that the best aspect of growing older was simply "enjoying life," a commentary on her present satisfaction level. Another woman felt more mature and linked more independence in the supported living model to a benefit of aging.

For one woman, having her brother and sister-in-law move away from her city was a concern, although it wasn't directly related to her aging. Having lost her father, and her mother in declining health, her brother's planned move created anxiety and uncertainty about the future. She recognized that she would not be seeing him as much.

4

Aging parents

The lives of parents and children are inextricably linked throughout their lifetime. Regardless of the role they play, parents affect, and are affected by, the quality of life of their adult child with PWS. As parents age, their concerns change and often become more urgent.

Family demographics

Family constellations change as people age. For 11 of the over-40 group (85 %), the parent relationships had changed since childhood. In other words, most of the group had experienced the loss of one of their parents through death, divorce or separation.

Mothers. The ages of the mothers of the 13 individuals profiled in this document ranged from 62 to 92 years. Only one of the mothers was still employed. Five of the mothers were now widows, three more were single parents. One mother was deceased. Only two individuals had their biological parents in intact marriages. Siblings described the hardships that some mothers had faced through single-parenting multiple children, including one with special needs.

Fathers. Two natural fathers and one step-father were still involved in the life of their adult child. One other father, a widower, was in the same city and saw his son only on occasion. There was evidence of male substitutes

Table 5 Number of children in PWS families	
No. of children	No of families
1	0
2	5
3	3
4	0
5	2
6	0
7	2
unknown	1

active in the lives of some individuals: an uncle as co-guardian, two cases of brothers as guardians, and a brother-in-law active in day-to-day support.

Siblings. No one in the over-40 group came from a single child family. As can be seen in Table 5, the number of children in families ranged from 2 to 7. In 4 instances the child with PWS was the first born to the family (Table 6). In 6 instances, the child with PWS was the last born.

In 7 situations siblings were actively involved in the lives of their sisters and brothers with PWS. For example, they lived close by and visited regularly, or they took on guardianship responsibilities.

Table 6 Ordinal position of adult with PWS	
Birth order of PWS adult	Number of families
First	4
Second	3
Third	1
Fourth	0
Fifth	2
Sixth	1
Seventh	1
Unknown	1

The average number of children born to the over-40 group families was 3.5. A trend to smaller families was evident when compared to a similar sized group of PWS families from the 1970s and 1980s in the author's file.

Uncertainties

This group of older parents have faced many uncertainties throughout the lives of their children. First there was the uncertainty related to diagnosis. Some had sought help for years before getting a diagnosis. An entry from a mother's diary in 1965 illustrates the uncertain future. Six months after her son's birth she wrote: "Doctor says there is no hope and no treatment. Most probably he will die young of pneumonia." This mother, like others, resolved to work hard to prove the doctors wrong.

For some the uncertainties had to do with the prevailing best practices and the recommendation for placement in an institution or group home. While some accepted the professional advice, others did not. Now, many years later, there is still emotion attached to the experiences. With out-of-home placements there were many questions, for example: Would they be able to visit? Would they still have a voice in the life of their child? Would the future be stable? The concerns associated with future care, after their own passing, represented the greatest of the uncertainties.

One mother related how her son's name had been on the Community Living housing list for several years, but that she and her husband had always made it clear that unless a lockable kitchen could be guaranteed, which for a long time was against the agency philosophy, they could not accept a placement. As a consequence, they lived with the uncertainty of a possible placement for their son until he was 30 years old. Uncertainties about residential placement issues were frequently cited as a source of stress by parents.

Residential peace of mind

When an adult with PWS leaves the family home the parents want to remain a part of his or her life. There is always parental anxiety over the level and quality of care. Parents and family identified the following effective residential supports which contributed to their peace of mind:

- *individualized support options* - having choices which take into consideration the individual's strengths and needs
- *caring and stable staff* - having staff that enjoy their job, are committed to providing quality care, and genuinely care about the individual with PWS as evidenced by such things as long term commitment, established family friendships, and going the extra mile on occasion
- *attitude of inclusiveness* - an attitude which values the participation of family as part of the support circle
- *professionalism* - residential care providers who are not threatened by the expertise of the parents and who don't have a know-it-all attitude.

Parents/caregivers also identified some negative themes which detracted from their own quality of life:

- *inexperienced or under-qualified staff* - having to work with staff who lack experience with, or specific knowledge about, PWS
- *waiting time* - the excessive delays involved in obtaining a desired outcome, usually a program or service, from a government ministry or service agency
- *staff management* - the problems associated with hiring, supervising and firing staff when working with the option of individualized service dollars
- *future care* - the uncertainties and anxiety associated with long-term care arrangements (e.g., housing investment, agency choice, local economics, political will).

Similar to the family members' vision expressed in the Community Living Research Project (2008), parents and family wanted a stable living environment for the PWS member. Stability contributes to parental peace of mind.

Need for advocacy

In all but one case parents and/or siblings continue to be actively involved in the lives of this over-40 group. There is commonly an on-going, life-long parental concern for the welfare of their child. "Who will look out for the future needs of my child?" surfaced in some form in most interviews. It was not so much the care needs that were of concern, rather it was the advocacy needs. After a lifetime of advocacy which included educating educators and social workers, fighting for issues of rights, seeking out opportunities for integration, and mediating transgressions in the community, parents fear there will be a lack of such advocacy when they are no longer around.

Concern for the future

One widow explained that her daughter had to be under the care of an agency in case anything happened to herself. She recognized the importance of continuity in her daughter's life. A couple, providing care to four adults with special needs, including a brother with PWS, worried about their own aging and questioned what would happen when they retire. They couldn't see any alternative residential options in their city to address PWS needs.

Another widow, aged 90, valued continued involvement in her daughter's life, and at the time of the last interview expressed displeasure that siblings had insisted on formally taking guardianship responsibilities. This sibling initiative was timely as within the year their mother had a stroke.

In six cases families had formally identified siblings as future guardians. In one situation parents did not want this responsibility to be placed on a sibling and made arrangements for future care through a faith-based agency. This included management of a condominium purchased by the parents to provide housing for their child. While other families felt confident in the long-term agency management of the adult's day and residential programs, arrangements for future guardianship were less clear.

Concerns about "the system"

Concerns about the system have been most strongly described by one mother and her daughter in a book by Kinash (2007). The mother felt that the system had "duped" her into believing that it had the answers for her daughter's best care. She says that the system placed her daughter at great, even life threatening, risk. At 40, the daughter is now leading a safer, healthier lifestyle, because of the advocacy of her mother.

In analyzing open-ended responses to the word "attitudes," from persons with PWS and their families, Kinash identifies human services workers and medical staff, particularly General Practitioners, as "perpetrators of disabling attitudes" which reinforce disability. To be fair, the criticism of human service workers applied more to the adult system and the criticism of medical practitioners more to the child system. Similar to Kinash, the present study found examples of attitudes by professional care workers that seemed to be self-serving and not necessarily putting the interests of the client first. Notably, however, the complaints related to earlier stages of life. There were few criticisms of current professional service providers.

Another major concern about the system had to do with government reduction in funding and the resulting inability of individuals and agencies to attract and retain qualified staff. This created undue stress on two families in the over-40 group and numerous younger families, and was most evident in stories from Alberta and Manitoba.

A third area of concern had to do with a lack of individualized options. Having to accept existing group-funded day and residential programs was not attractive to some parents, but they felt that they had no other options. Within the over-40 parent group there were those who passively accepted what was offered by the system, and there were those who challenged the system and advocated for other options.

Parent quality of life

Parent testimonies suggest that parent quality of life is directly linked to the quality of care provided for their child. One parent expressed appreciation for "the safety net of a home and workplace with 24 hour security." She also valued the "programs built around PWS and a community of caring people." Another mother described an improvement in accommodation, stating that "I can sleep at night now." Night supervision was important, otherwise her daughter would be out or on the phone. She went on to say that "improvement is so marked." Confidence in the safety net, the level of supervision by caring people is essential to providing peace of mind for parents.

Being able to spend time in a normalized family relationship adds to parent quality of life. For adults with PWS living outside of the family home, the chance to visit home in the same manner as siblings is important. For one mother, sharing a weekly meal together with her son on a set schedule is a valued ritual. One young man took it upon himself to do simple chores when he returned for a weekly visit, something that was appreciated by his parents. One mother and daughter, living in different communities, speak on the phone almost daily. As with other families, the daughter returns home on festive occasions to participate with her parents and siblings. For families of faith, being able to see their son or daughter at their place of worship weekly is important.

Individuals living with parents or other family members have daily opportunity for meaningful interactions. Parents spoke with pride about the quality of relationships that PWS adults have with siblings, nieces and nephews. They similarly spoke proudly about the manner in which siblings have taken on responsibilities to care for the adult with PWS.

Parents also speak with pride about the community involvements and personal accomplishments of the adult with PWS. The successes of children bring satisfaction to parents. There is a sense that despite all of the parenting problems of childhood some things must have been done right. There is also the sense that there has been success despite all of the negatives that they had read about in the literature. Parents feel good about their own accomplishments in the face of such early gloom.

Reaching a stage where they can enjoy their own independence with the knowledge that their son or daughter is being adequately cared for is perhaps the biggest factor in parents' own quality of life. The belief that they can participate in social and leisure activities or to take a holiday is liberating and adds quality to their lives, even if they do not always take advantage of it.

Having the assurance that they can leave this life with the knowledge that their offspring will be well cared for brings a peace of mind that contributes immeasurable to their quality of life.

Parents' quality of life may be supported through formal affiliation or involvement with PWS organizations. They can be a source for resources, conferences, the latest research, and networking opportunities with other parents (see Appendix). Even though some parents choose not to affiliate with local, regional or provincial groups, most take advantage of membership in the American or international associations in order to keep abreast of the latest PWS information.

5

Profiles

This chapter contains 13 profiles of Canadians with PWS who are beyond their fortieth birthday. They represent rural and urban settings across four provinces.

Angela

After years of being "in the system," and numerous attempts at different residential models in the city environment, Angela and her mother, Doris, decided to relocate to a small rural acreage in Alberta. The closest neighbor is a half a kilometre away. "It is peaceful here," says Angela, "and there are no smells from restaurants to torment me."

Both Angela and Doris are angry at the way the adult system deluded them. The system insisted that Angela would be better off living away from her mother's home in a more independent fashion, but did not provide the required supports that would make it successful. The service providers vacillated between total freedom, which demanded impossible self-control, and strict external controls which stripped her of the sense of self-control and dignity which she had developed over the years. The resulting morbid obesity placed Angela at death's door. Angela says that the worse thing was being so close to

thinking she was going to die.   They both feel that taking controls away from the system saved Angela's life.   At the farm they have been able to get back to what worked for Angela and regain stability in their lives.   Eventually, Doris and Angela found a service provider who listens and provides the required supports, and both say that life is good again.

Angela started to learn about the importance of nutrition and how to count calories when she was twelve years old. This has served her well as now she manages all of her menu planning, grocery shopping and food preparation with the support of staff supervision. Understanding how to count calories and nutritional requirements allows her the opportunities to make informed choices, which impact her self-esteem. She says it gives her the feeling that she has lots of control over her life. Her kitchen is specially designed to support her needs. The eating area is separated from the preparation and food storage area by a regular, *but lockable,* door. Angela says it feels more normal this way and there doesn't need to be locks on cup-boards or chains on the fridge. "I really like it this way because it makes people think I am 'normal' when they visit my home." When she is home alone she prepares and keeps the appropriate amounts of food outside of the locked kitchen area.

Presently, Angela's weight is around 140 pounds but she is working hard to reach her goal of 130. She records her weight on a calendar. Angela says that exercise is very important, not only for weight management but also because she wants to have a firmer and sexier looking body. She is proud that she is self-motivated to work out at the gym. She says that she never felt motivated when a staff was telling her that she should exercise. "When they stopped telling me what to do, I found a gym and a really good fitness instructor that sets my program and I am loving it." She does two hour work-outs four or five times a week.

Angela has been an enthusiastic clogger for the past five years. She has a keen sense of rhythm and is able to clog for as long as three hours at a time. She is proud to be the captain of her bowling team, in a mixed league. Both of these activities take place with fully inte-grated groups. She also is a member of the Royal Canadian Legion and loves to go there with her friends.

Walking without supervision was never an option when Angela lived in the city. Now she has two dogs that she can take for walks whenever she chooses, without staff accompanying her.

Angela took training to be a "caring clown" and named herself "Blossom." She feels appreciated when she volunteers at the hospital as Blossom or as a "pet therapist" (one of her dogs is extremely good at visiting people). She also loves playing cribbage with an elderly lady in extended care. Angela sees herself as a self-advocate and an advocate for people with disabilities. She has developed her presentation material based on personal experiences and welcomes opportunities to present. She has made presentations to rehabilitation students, teachers and agencies. She did work at a part-time job for four years when she lived in the city, but today she feels more valued when she volunteers in her community.

Doris proudly says that Angela is self-motivated and spends hours practicing her piano lessons. She enjoys playing the piano and loves the piano teacher that she found in 1991. Angela is very good at crocheting – making items that she sells or gives as gifts. Besides her two dogs, she owns two llamas, two cats, and sometimes some baby kittens.

Angela is in control of her own staffing. She interviews and hires only those workers who understand and treat her with respect. She and her mother wrote a handout titled "How to Support Me," which is very specific about how Angela wants to be supported and which is given to prospective staff. In her words, "I need workers who understand the things that torment my brain so that's why I try hard to let them know, so I don't fail. I wouldn't do things to torment the people I care about."

Angela's story has been documented in *A Recipe for Success* by Shelly Kinash (2007). Both Angela and Doris are now enjoying more relaxed lifestyles and higher quality of lives than they experienced in an urban setting. In Angela's words, "I live independently. I am a 40 year old adult. I am living on a farm. I finally feel that I have freedom and less controls and more choices – I love my life."

Ann

Ann was not diagnosed with PWS until age 24. At 46, she has experienced a range of living situations: residential school, integrated group home, PWS-specific group home, supported independent living, living with parents, and living with another family. She has lived in two countries, two provinces, urban and rural settings, and even on a small island. Having spent most of her life in the U.S.A., she came to Canada to be close to her mother and stepfather. Immigration was a long and costly process. Initially she was denied entry because she did not meet admissibility criteria. Eventually, with changes to immigration criteria, she became eligible.

After living in Ontario her parents relocated to Vancouver Island, and then to an even smaller island, believing it would be a safe environment for Ann. With 300 residents and only one commercial establishment it seemed ideal. There was a strong sense of community and Ann enjoyed the social life. However, nobody locked their doors, which lead to some food issues and need for restrictions. Eventually, Ann opted to live with experienced caregivers in Nanaimo. Here Ann is very happy, and speaks highly of her caregivers. "They are kind. They speak nicely and slowly so I can understand. They help me with my problems." And most importantly, she says, "they have a sense of humour."

Ann says that locks make her feel like she is in a jailhouse. Presently, there are no locks. There is one rule: she cannot go into the kitchen without anyone else there. Her bedroom is on the lower level of a split level home, which she says "helps me a lot" as it is away from the flow of traffic to the kitchen.

During the day Ann attends a workshop where she enjoys latch hooking. She admits to incidents of taking food, but insists that she can control herself so long as she does not see food. She does not handle money or go to stores alone.

While described as being very healthy, Ann does have considerable difficulty with her knees, making walking painful. She has had three knee surgeries and has been told she will not be eligible for a knee replacement until somewhere in her fifties. She rides a stationary bike daily for exercise and has a weekly weigh-in. Currently she weighs 180 pounds.

Ann enjoys swimming and bowling with Special Olympics. She takes piano lessons and loves playing the piano. She has a keyboard at her day program and practices every day. At home she enjoys playing cards, listening to music, and watching television or DVDs.

Two of her favourite actors are Michael Landon and Victor French, stars she met while they were filming a "Highway to Heaven" segment in her neighbourhood when she was living in California. She avidly does word search puzzles, and jigsaw puzzles of any size.

Ann functions best when she has choices and can negotiate. She cooperates when given the opportunity to engage in joint problem solving and responds well to praise. She recognizes her own anxieties and acknowledges the beneficial effects of Paxil. Ann has been described as a "sunshine girl" with an "infectious presence."

Ann Marie

The youngest of five children, Ann Marie resided in Michener Centre, a provincial institution for people with mental handicaps, from age 12 to 24. When she came out of the Centre she carried 280 pounds on her 4 foot 6 inch frame. Today, on a diet of 900-1000 calories, her weight is maintained at about 137 pounds.

It was not until age 26, while living with L'Arche, that she was finally diagnosed with PWS. A short time later she transferred to the SKILLS Society. This agency has been providing her residential and day program for 19 years.

When asked if she had a message for younger families she replied "tell them how I am enjoying life" and "how important it is to be active." At 57, with rods in her back for scoliosis, leg braces and crutches, Ann Marie is very active. Her individualized day program with her support worker involves exercise, meal planning, grocery shopping, food preparation, and social-recreational activities. She enjoys volunteer activities, outings in the community, cultural events, and shopping. She has even participated in a couple of political protests. Because of her love of animals dog-walking has been built into her exercise program. She enjoys it when other tenants bring their cats to visit.

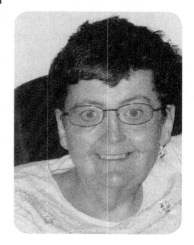

In the evening she enjoys visiting with friends, sharing coffee, music (Elvis, Anne Murray, Country & Western), old movies (John

Wayne, Elvis Presley) or board games ("Trouble" is her favourite). When watching television she keeps her hands active by knitting. She has enjoyed major travel trips to: Japan and Korea with L'Arche, and separate trips to Disneyworld and Disneyland with the SKILLS Society. Her support worker says that she wouldn't hesitate to travel with her again – "she is so much fun to be with." After working with Ann Marie for ten years Christina has become close to the family.

Ann Marie enjoys good health, an active lifestyle and the support of staff, family and friends. She sees her mother weekly and enjoys outings with her sisters. Those closest to her say that she has mellowed with age and is a delight to be around. She is more relaxed, less anxious and doesn't get upset as easily as in earlier years.

Ann Marie lives in a one bedroom apartment in a very secure building administered by the SKILLS Society. Each unit is alarmed to let the night staff know of any activity. Her mail is monitored (she got a credit card through the mail once) and she requires a co-signer for her banking.

The perpetual smile on Ann Marie's face is testimony to her enjoyment of life.

Bill

In 1986, at age 26, Bill's weight was out of control - at 4 feet 11 inches he weighed 386 pounds. Without intervention, the prognosis was that he would only have days to live.

After three months of hospitalization and 150 pounds of weight loss Bill was placed in a group home for clients with developmental disabilities. Food continued to be an issue, his weight vacillated, and he struggled with a system of rewards and punishments. Family style meals where others could help themselves while Bill's plate was apportioned beforehand with small amounts (calorie counted) was a totally frustrating issue. There were bouts of stealing at the day program, and in the community, and Bill was treated for psychological issues.

In 1993, a second group home placement was more successful. He enjoyed some sports activities, was willing to take more risks and consequently gained more confidence. He enjoyed a full and active lifestyle, including a day program, daily visits to the YMCA and a girlfriend. Despite progress, however, his weight still vacillated and he still had problems with stealing food.

In 1996, at age 36, Bill went to live with his sister and her family. Brenda and her husband subsequently relocated and opened their home to other adults with special needs as well. In 2000, Bill was prescribed Bupropion (Wellbutrin) and lost 40 pounds over the next three months. Two years later, he weighed between 130 and 135 pounds. Brenda feels that the success of Wellbutrin has been in relieving Bill's anxiety. Along with anxiety re-

duction came more appropriate eating habits, less manipulation and greater happiness. Bill enjoys a good relationship with his doctor and visits his office weekly for a weigh-in.

At home Bill is responsible for feeding the animals (bird, dog, cat), keeping the birdcage clean, taking out the garbage and recycling. His favourite activity is walking the dog. He also helps his housemates to keep track of their money. They all have access to their money, but must always produce receipts for purchases. Bill and Brenda both feel that the living situation is working well. Meals are planned around the diabetic exchange and Weight Watcher diets. Bill can make food choices. His meals, however, are always served to him – and his plate is as full as anyone else's. When he snacks, he can choose from "free foods," that is to say "the good vegetables." Because his weight is well-managed, he is allowed treats.

Bill is now 49 years old. He is engaged to Maggie, a woman with Down syndrome who also lives in the house. They keep an active social life. Bill manages public transportation well so they are able to attend events in the city.

Bill is in good health and only requires iron supplements. He is physically very active and never complains of being sore or tired. He walks three miles round trip each day to work and walks the dog regularly. He has made two trips to the Special Olympics national games to compete in the sport of curling.

The only area where Bill's desires are unmet is in the area of employment. "I would love to be working at a real job like some of my friends," he says, "especially in a pet store or bussing tables at Starbucks." Instead, he attends a day program, where there is little challenge, except when he gets to choose options. For several years he has been participating weekly on-air with a radio show broadcast by the local university. "Thrift Store Music" plays old songs, features special tributes and responds to special requests. He also enjoys the weekly Animal Extravaganza Program where he is involved in showing animals at local malls. Once a month he helps to make soup for a neighbourhood community project. When asked if he had any advice to share, Bill thoughtfully responded with "Do activities in the community. It takes your mind off food and reduces anxiety."

Bill is very happy with his life today. He knows that what he eats can hurt him and he doesn't like to think about the past. In his words, "I don't swear, but PWS is a pain in the butt." Brenda and her husband echoed the sentiment, but added "PWS has taught us a lot."

Brenda

At age 23 Brenda married "a good guy, but he drank too much." After four years the marriage ended in divorce. Later, she had a common-law relationship that lasted 1.5 years. Unfortunately, her partner took advantage of her financially and recurring health concerns caused her parents to bring her home. She has been living with her parents for the last 10 years.

Brenda acquired her driver's license at age 17. In 25 years she has only had one ticket, for exceeding the limit in a school zone. She doesn't drive far now, only to the mall or to the Legion. She plans her routes carefully and carries a cell phone for safety. When she was younger, she would drive from her parents' home in Port Alberni to Campbell River (a drive of over two hours) where she lived for several years.

While she doesn't telephone or go out much, Brenda does go to the Legion where she has friends. As a member of the Ladies Auxiliary she attends the monthly luncheon meeting and helps with the bingos and bazaars. She is polite, verbal and outgoing. She enjoys a relaxed, joking relationship with her parents. She also enjoys her brother and family who live close by.

Brenda has participated in work training programs and has worked for short terms in the past, but now considers herself to be retired. She acknowledges age-related anxiety, hearing and memory problems. She sometimes forgets to take her meds and needles. Her health is stable but of concern. She has Type I diabetes and administers her own injections. She has an occasional night-time seizure and, in winter, suffers from asthma. She's been a smoker for more than 20 years.

The computer is an important part of Brenda's daily life. She is competent at using e-mail, Facebook, word processing and a variety of games. She has her own computer and television. Everyday she does a word search or crossword puzzle with her morning coffee. She is also working on learning to read patterns as she knits. She likes to read, particularly books by Danielle Steele. She collects books, pens, and cat ornaments.

Brenda is 4 feet 9 inches tall, wears size 2 shoes and weighs 185 pounds. Her weight has been stable for the last 20 years. Food is not locked in the home. Basically, she follows the diabetic diet. From her parents' perspective the food drive is not an issue. Brenda largely self-regulates, and when her parents are away she is responsible for her own food. She relies more on the microwave than on the stove for preparing meals.

At 44 Brenda expresses satisfaction with her single life, living situation, and social activities.

Darcy

Darcy left public school at age 21 and shortly thereafter moved from home to go into a six-person group home. Life in the group home was challenging for him. He had a full schedule which included: a workshop program, Special Olympics sports activities, monthly Peoples' First meetings, and alternate weekends at home. Darcy found it increasingly difficult to be on a strict diet while the others ate generously. After six years in the group home the situation became intolerable and he moved back home.

After living in his mother's home for 3.5 years, Darcy was placed in a rented house under a new, parent-operated agency. At this point he weighed 225 pounds. He was paired with another young man

with PWS, ten years his junior. While assumptions were made about how this placement should work, it didn't work out to their mutual benefit.

After a year Darcy was moved into his own accommodation. Hearthstone Community Group purchased a mobile home in a trailer park in town, which was more economical than an apartment or house. It has worked well because it is in a quiet neighbourhood. Darcy has the master bedroom. The wall between the two smaller bedrooms was removed to provide an office and sleeping area for overnight staff. The only concern is for the periodic strong wind activity in the area in recent years. For the last five years he has had a special radio system to monitor weather and get alerts.

At 46, Darcy is generally in good health. His weight is stable at 160 pounds, almost half what it was in his early twenties. Due to the loss of several friends and relatives, which he experienced at a young age, Darcy has required medications to assist with his adjustment. He has had three hernia surgeries. In the early 90s he fell on the hardwood floor and stretched a ligament requiring a leg brace for many years. Physical activity became limited to chair exercises. He was fortunate to have a couple of different ladies host crafts in their home for him for several years. Darcy now uses a walker regularly and a wheelchair for special outings and Special Olympics bowling.

Church has been a constant throughout Darcy's life. It is a source of pride and contributes to his self-esteem. He enjoys his role as an usher, taking the collection. His worker takes him to church and they sit in front of his mother. He gets a strong sense of personal support from the church. Pastors assist with counselling when needed and take him out for coffee on occasion.

For 12.5 years Darcy worked at "his job" as a volunteer busboy in a family restaurant. He worked for two hours on Wednesday and Sunday afternoons, for which he received an honourarium of five dollars. The Assistant Manager "took him on" and provided close supervision. There were a few food issues over the years but they were overcome. He has now "retired," but misses his job.

At home, Darcy enjoys making plastic bead necklaces and collecting dog ornaments. In earlier years he used to sell necklaces for two dollars whenever he could, now he presents them as key chain gifts. He likes card and board games (such as Fish, Snakes & Ladders, Monopoly, Bingo, and Crazy 8s) and is keen to win. He has never enjoyed jigsaw puzzles beyond 15 or 20 pieces. He likes to see the Shriners in parades and to watch family movies and cartoons (especially Barney). He likes the colour blue and thrives on polka music. Since 1994 he has taken great pleasure in playing Santa Claus for the Hearthstone Christmas parties.

Darcy has always had strong support from his mother. He still goes home to have dinner with her once each week, for four hours from 3:30 to 7:30. He is very proud of his three nephews. He has a very reliable memory for immediate family birthdays and special occasions and always mails a card. He enjoys going for coffee with his worker. At Christmas and for birthdays family give him McDonald's gift cards so that he can go for coffee. This allows him some independence without the stress of handling money. He is a very social person and lots of people know him in the community.

David

Since finishing high school David has had daily work at ARC Industries, where piecemeal work is done for local businesses. When candy and holiday foods are packaged during the Christmas season David is given alternative work in a different area where he will not be tempted.

David, now 44, lived at home until he was 30 years old. While his name had been on the local Community Living housing list for several years, his parents had made it clear that unless a locked kitchen could be guaranteed they would only accept a placement in case of dire family emergency. For a long time this was against the agency philosophy but David's parents continued to advocate for a PWS-specific group home. In his mother's words, "you can imagine our joy and relief when the Board unexpectedly agreed to all our requests the year we moved into our retirement condo when David was 30!"

While parents worried about the trauma he would experience on leaving home, he came home the day after he first heard the news and announced, "You can start packing my clothes, mother. I'm out of here Friday night...they have a place for me at Headon House!"

Headon House and ARC Industries are both part of the same parent organization. The Community Living Board hired a psychologist to set up a behaviour program for both the workshop and the home, which has been very successful. At Headon House David is responsible for making his bed and keeping his bedroom neat, personal cleanliness and grooming, and maintaining his weight at an appropriate level by exercising. The Community Living Board also engaged a nutritionist familiar with PWS to set up the food program and give cooking lessons to the staff. David's weight is stable at 150-154 pounds and he has excellent health. Staff at the group home carry out a weekly weigh-in with charted records.

In recent years the group home has provided more in-house programming, but David gets most of his exercise on weekends with special needs workers. He enjoys swimming and hiking. Friday night is games night at Headon House. David especially likes Bingo, where he wins prizes like shaving cream, comb or socks. According to his mother he is "a whiz" at Scrabble and card games. He also enjoys music, and has a tape collection of everything from the Irish Rovers to bagpipes and hymns. His favourite videos are of the "Little House on the Prairie" variety. His favourite television program is "Coronation Street."

David's mother lives only three blocks from her son and is deeply involved in his life. David visits her three times per week. On Wednesdays he goes to put the garbage out, something that he initiated to help his parents before his father passed away. He also likes to collect the mail from the group mail box. He usually goes home for an overnight visit on weekends.

After 12 years at Headon House David's mother wrote, "I feel our son has the best of all possible worlds – work that he likes, the safety net of a home (and workplace) with 24 hour security and programs built around Prader-Willi syndrome, and a community of caring people who understand his syndrome but appreciate him for the person he really is." David brags about how lucky he is to have two homes where people really understand him.

Kip

An article in *British Columbia Report* magazine (Carter, 1991) described the desire of a 27 year old young man with PWS to get out of Alberta's Michener Centre, a provincial institution with more than 1,000 residents with mental handicaps. The article was titled "An appetite for freedom." After 10 years as a resident Kip wanted out. He wanted to be able to go to the movies or go to an Edmonton Eskimos football game.

According to the article, Kip became his own advocate, writing the local newspaper, phoning government officials and contacting Legal Aid for advice. Centre staff, his doctor and the Public Guardian all said that he would be happier in the outside world. The main drawback was the cost for 24 hour supervision. His doctor described him as depressed due to the frustration with funding.

A second article (PDD, 2008) describes how he recently moved into his current home* in Innisfail operated by PROS (Providing Residential Options and Services), where he has one-to-one staff, and a safe and supportive environment. He is now happy in his own place. He is able to do some of his own cooking. He has more freedom and choices of things to do.

Kip has had two heart attacks. Today he is eating healthier with more vegetables and salads. "His weight dropped from 248 lbs to 178 and he no longer needs to drag a cart with an oxygen tank wherever he goes." Portable oxygen only goes along on outings as a precaution. He walks six blocks every morning, attends aquacize fitness sessions, and swims three or four times each week. His success is based on two essentials, exercise and diet.

Only healthy foods are allowed in the home, and the same food restrictions apply to staff as well as to Kip. Food is stored behind locked doors. "We don't blame Kip if he weakens" says the PROS operator. "We ask him, 'where did we screw up?'" She adds, "I'm very proud of Kip. He has made major changes in his life. He wants to show people he can succeed so he can remain in the community."

[*Kip moved into the community at age 42.]

LeeAnne

At 42, LeeAnne enjoys living in her own apartment with attendant support. After years of shared accommodation, which hadn't always been comfortable, she now has her own space. While the one bedroom apartment requires a cot to be set up each night for a staff person, it otherwise provides adequate living space. Walls display favourite jigsaw puzzles which have been mounted. She has a personal computer, television, and a pair of finches. She proudly displays her

crocheting, rug-hooking, and knitting accomplishments. LeeAnne also excitedly shows off her engagement ring and talks fondly of her fiancé, a man she met through her day program.

Lately her activities have become more sedentary due to some health issues. She has arthritis and a knee which gives out on her on occasion. She also had a pulmonary embolism two years ago and is on medications for diabetes. Her weight is 239 pounds and monitored with a weekly weigh-in.

LeeAnne attends a workshop where she is involved in vocational and recreation/leisure activities. She particularly enjoys doing crafts and paid contract jobs. She prefers independent tasks and has been acknowledged by staff for her attention to detail. She has a lot of self-confidence and is definitely a "take charge" type of person. She gets anxious, however, about change and needs ample warning. Both her residential accommodation and day program are administered by Rehoboth Christian Ministries.

LeeAnne always gets home from work in time to watch her favourite soap opera, "The Young and The Restless." When she is watching TV she keeps busy with crocheting so that she doesn't skin-pick. In the evenings she may visit with a friend downstairs, enjoying coffee, listening to music or painting her nails. One night each week she receives tutoring for upgrading her schooling. Her favourite recreation activity is fishing, an activity that her older brother introduced her to years ago.

The fifth of six children, LeeAnne grew up in rural communities in Alberta. She left home and went to live in a group home in her early twenties. She didn't always enjoy her group and shared living accommodations and is adamant that she would never live in a PWS-specific group home. She identifies "living independently with staff support" as her greatest accomplishment. This, she says "was worth fighting for." Those around her see LeeAnne mellowing and credit the more independent living situation rather than her increasing age. LeeAnne talks with her mother almost daily on the telephone and returns to the family home in a neighbouring community to celebrate special occasions.

Madeline

Up to May 2008, Madeline was happy living in her basement bed/sitting room in the home of a former program worker. This arrangement had lasted 12 years until Corinne retired and left the area. Madeline, now 49, has a similar arrangement with Sharon and is hoping that it will also last several years.

As Madeline explains, "I can be independent downstairs." She has her own television and can watch her own programs, but can participate upstairs with the family when she wants. She generally eats her meals upstairs, including lunch when she is home; if she is watching a particular television show, she is happy to have supper in her own area. All of the cooking is done for her.

Madeline has lived in group homes, shared accommodations with a roommate, and independently with attendant support. She says that she likes the current arrangement the best.

Each day Madeline goes out to work at volunteer roles in the community. She is responsible for making all of her own arrangements. She does clerical work for a number of non-profit societies (e,g., Red Cross, Alzheimer Society, Cancer Society, and the Kidney Foundation). She uses a computer to work with donor lists, stuffs envelopes, photocopies and collates materials. She has a day worker who accompanies her to the job sites to monitor food and social situations. Madeline is disappointed when there is no work for a day.

Sharon monitors Madeline's weight weekly. Currently weight is maintained at about 150 pounds. Exercise includes dog-walking with Sharon, walks with her day worker, and weekly bowling with Special Olympics during the fall and winter.

Madeline's parents were leaders in the PWS parent organization for many years. Because of this, she attended many PWS conferences, including those in the U.S.A, and the annual camps at the William Watson Lodge.

Madeline regularly carries a crossword, word search, or sidoku book with her to fill idle time. She has a good vocabulary. In the evenings she likes to watch TV. She can converse on a wide range of topics.

On Sundays, one of her siblings (she is the youngest of seven) provides transportation to church and then arranges for Madeline to spend time with her mother. Involvement in her Catholic faith community has been important throughout her adult life, particularly involvement in the Faith and Light Community. But she laments, "it is difficult to get around Calgary." She finds it hard to rely on the generosity of family and others if she wants to go somewhere.

Madeline's father died five years ago and her mother is in mid stage Alzheimer's and is currently in long term care. Two siblings now share guardianship for Madeline.

Margaret

Margaret lives in a two bedroom apartment with 24/7 attendant support. She has been under the care of the SCOPE Society for more than ten years. Her residence, and until recently her staffing, have been stable over this time period. One staff person quit, however, to take a higher-paying job at a supermarket and the agency was having difficulty trying to replace her. The lack of staff placed an extra burden for supervision on her guardians. One worker, has been with her for more than five years. She has become an extended family member and sometimes takes Margaret home with her for weekends.

Tyler, Margaret's younger sister, and an uncle have taken over as guardians in the last three years. Margaret and Tyler meet every Monday evening to go over her personal goals. Uncle Leonard also visits her regularly.

At 47, Margaret's weight is stable at 124 pounds on a 1000-1200 calorie diet. In her early 30s she had weighed 300 pounds. She is proud of her weight and the activities that she can now do.

Margaret expresses satisfaction with her lifestyle. She identifies "living in my own apartment" as one of the best things about her life. According to her worker, at times Margaret will break into song spontaneously at home. She leads an active lifestyle focusing on social-recreational activities. Her weekly schedule includes: Tuesdays at Indefinite Arts (ceramics, painting), exercise (walking, dancing, swimming, exercise workouts), special outings (e.g., library, Callaway Park, Calgary Stampede), and social activities (e.g., bowling, dinner with a friend). At home she enjoys: watching movies, doing puzzles, and hooking rugs.

Her apartment is well-equipped with electronics - TV, VCR, DVD and computer. Margaret is a prolific collector of videos and DVDs. Her collection of 451 titles is attractively mounted on wall shelving and systematically arranged. The walls neatly display mounted puzzles, family photos and recognition plaques. In her bedroom she has a collection of international dolls.

Those closest to Margaret feel that she has been maturing in the last five years. She is now more empathetic, easier to talk to and negotiate with. Her self-esteem has increased. "She is more sure of herself as a worthwhile person, enabling her to interact more with others." It used to be that she was hospitalized and sedated almost annually, but this has not happened in the last eight years.

Margaret requires full-time attendant support for supervision to control food access and to prevent skin picking and stealing. Margaret did not grow up with locks for food access control. Now the food storage cupboard is locked, the entrance door has a childproof knob, and the bedroom door has a bell alarm. Until restrictive duct-taped gloves were introduced, a weekly trip to a wound clinic was part of the routine to cope with severe skin-picking. Staff handle all money transactions.

Tyler and Margaret took their first ever trip together last year, a 7-day trip and cruise to Disneyworld. In Tyler's words, "I'm glad that she got to do it, but we would never do it again." The travel component was fine, but food was too available on the cruise. Margaret proudly shares her photo memories of the trip. She also proudly shares the pictures of Tyler's wedding, where she had the role as Maid of Honour. Margaret and Tyler are now sharing a special relationship that they did not experience in earlier life.

[*Margaret passed away on December 30, 2009, ten days before her 48th birthday, after a brief battle with pneumonia.*]

Paul

Paul lives in a three bedroom townhouse, which is shared with another young man and staff. His residential and day programs are supervised by Rehoboth Christian Ministries. He has an individualized day program. Each day he does volunteer work at different locations, largely for churches and schools, accompanied by his worker. According to his parents, he works best with a staff person who is "laid back" and who will accept him as he is and not try to fix him.

Paul left home 21 years ago at the age of 23. Twelve years later the doctor prescribed Prozac to assist with his emotions and behaviour. His parents say that this was a very positive development as he is less agitated now and no longer has temper issues.

Paul gets a balanced diet and regular exercise. Healthy eating and physical activity are cornerstones of his well-being. He gets physical activity by sweeping and mopping on some jobs, as well as walking with his worker, and swimming every Friday. By being strict with his diet he is allowed to have treats once in a while. He stands 5 feet 4 inches tall and weighs 131 pounds. He weighs himself every morning. Staff are required to sign daily that he has weighed in and done his exercises. His father graphs his weight.

Church and faith have always been important parts of Paul's life. He feels comfortable in the church. He enjoys singing at church and at home, and does so with accurate pitch. His faith assures him that each day the "slate" is wiped clean and he can start fresh again. Paul goes to church with his parents and visits them regularly.

Paul has always taken vacations with his parents. In recent years he has gone to Tofino, on the west coast of Vancouver Island, and to Hawaii with them. He has accompanied them to many PWS conferences over the years. Car travel is best when he sits up front with the map and acts as co-pilot, otherwise he falls asleep in the back seat. He also attends an annual Rehoboth camp in the summer.

According to his parents, Paul is more mellow now than in the past. While age may be a factor, it may also be related in part to more independent living or the prescription of Prozac. He responds best to encouragement and praise.

Paul's leisure activities include watching television, doing jigsaw puzzles, listening to music, and writing letters. When he visits his parents he likes to play Yahtzee and SKIP-BO. He likes to go to his parents' home for weekends. Paul has a fascination with weather and checks it regularly on the television.

Shelagh

Shelagh is the second oldest in a family of four children. With three brothers she has always been well protected. According to her mother, she has lead a fairly sheltered life. Family is very important to her. She loves the an-nual reunions, weddings, Christmas gatherings and time with her nieces. She has a sadness that she can't have babies, but follows this with "but I am mommy to Sammy" (her cat).

Shelagh enjoyed high school where she received special education supports. She received the diagnosis of PWS at age 19, the same year that she left school. After graduation she attended the adult special education program at North Island College for a year, and then entered the Arrowsmith Workshop for five years. She subse-quently moved to Parksville, returned to Port Alberni, and then went on to Victoria, each move with her family. While she tried group home living she did not like the experience. She is much happier living with family.

At age 28 Shelagh was diagnosed with diabetes. She also has scoliosis, but is otherwise in good health. She had her gall bladder removed a few years ago. She has taken Haldol all of her adult years, never having any successes with alternatives. Other drugs always made things worse and once she ended up in the hospital because of an adverse reaction. Shelagh began smoking at age 20 and smoked half a pack of cigarettes daily until recently, when she decided to quit "in order to be healthier." She is on a common sense diabetic diet.

When the family moved to Victoria Shelagh had to wait two years before getting into a workshop program. While she liked most of the activities, she didn't enjoy all of them. She particularly liked craft activities, such as making necklaces, bracelets and cards. For the past two years, however, she has chosen not to attend the workshop.

At home she enjoys doing bead work, watching movies, and

television, especially Judge Judy and Peoples' Court. On the weekends she likes to have a cup of tea with her dad and go for a walk. She likes to clean and tidy things and keeps her room neat. She collects purses, approaching friends, neighbours, and even strangers for their old purses. The purses are neatly kept with a trinket in each one.

Shelagh is proud of a framed piece of original art that her art teacher gave her at graduation and which is displayed prominently in the entranceway of the house. She also feels good about the various gifts which she has made for her mother.

According to her mother, there had been a mellowing in Shelagh's behaviours in the last five years. At 45, she is better able to handle changes and work through a crisis than previously.

When asked to name the most important people in her life, Shelagh did not hesitate in saying "my mom" and "Olive, my second mom." Olive was a respite worker that she became very fond of when she lived in Port Alberni.

[*Sadly, Shelagh's mother passed away recently. Shelagh now resides with a brother and sister-in-law. Relationships, particularly with family, continue to be an important part of Shelagh's support system and quality of life.*]

6

An autobiography

The story of John Symons which follows is an autobiography. It was written by John, at age 41, when he was invited to address the 1997 Ontario People First Conference. It is reproduced here in part, retaining John's spelling, punctuation, capitalization and underlining. John articulately describes what it is like to live with Prader-Willi syndrome.

Unfortunately, John died in December of the following year after being hospitalized for pneumonia. In honour of John's work, he was posthumously selected for The 1999 James Montgomerie Honour Award by the Ontario Association for Community Living. "This award is presented annually to a self-advocate who has demonstrated a commitment to the goals of people identified as having an intellectual disability." In a letter to John's mother, the President of the Association wrote: "there is no question that your son, John, demonstrated a commitment and a passion to people who struggle every day to gain acceptance as equal citizens. His work to educate people about Prader-Willi syndrome and his involvement in People First had a strong impact on many people."

John's legacy lives on. Janalee Heinemann, former Executive Director of the PWA-USA, in writing to John's mother, stated:

I cannot tell you how much John's words have impacted thousands of people. We use the page I created from his words in all of our crisis packets, in all of our awareness packets, in all of our PR packets, etc. There is not a day go by that he does not touch someone's heart.

John was one of the original participants in the 1985-86 study by the author. In the intervening years he moved from British Columbia to Ontario.

John

Hi, my name is John Hudson Symons. I was born in Toronto, on May 12, 1956, resided in British Columbia for a number of years, and since June 1996, I live in Whitby, Ontario.

I am a member of Hearts Family Network, Secretary of People's First Ajax-Pickering-Whitby and Member at large of People's First Ontario. I co-ordinate the Phone Friends Club and the newly created PALS Club through the Literacy Outreach Centre.

By sharing my story with you today, I feel that I am speaking on behalf of <u>all your children</u>, for those who can express their desires, and for those who cannot express themselves. <u>Please consider my past when planning your children's future as some situations may apply to your child</u>.

I want to help you understand how someone feels to live with a developmental disability and how you can help that person. Although I distinctly remember the names of people, places and dates of events, I will not identify people by name. I have prepared this presentation today and I will <u>read</u> the information to you so I do not omit any important facts.

I have a developmental disability known as Prader-Willi syndrome. This syndrome requires 24 hour care to manage the life threatening characteristics I face everyday. The chromosome deletion creates an insatiable appetite (we are always hungry), compounded by the inability to metabolize the caloric intake and behaviour difficulties. I will be distributing a flyer about Prader-Willi as you leave tonight.

People with developmental disabilities are human beings just like you. We have feelings, dreams and personal thoughts. We have a heart, soul, mind and spirit and we need you to understand us. Understanding and caring are two of the most important things that you can do for us.

I would like to talk about my disability and experiences and the effect it has had on my life. Prader-Willi syndrome was not discovered until 1956, so there was little known to all profession-als, while I was growing up. Although my father knew that I had Prader-Willi, he would not accept the fact.

I learned to talk and sing by 18 months of age and learned to read at four years of age. When I attended kindergarten I had to crawl up the front stairs as I did not have enough coordination at the time. I had a great fear of falling, and I still do to this day. The kids at school [were] cruel and mean. I only had 1/2 vision in my left eye and required surgery to correct my vision. I had to wear a patch on my eye before surgery, I guess you could say that I look like a pirate for awhile. However, the kids were mean and cruel. Teachers were also very cruel. I did not have any friends and at recess I was teased and kicked. I had no one invite me over to their house or to play with dur-ing or after school. I often picked open sores that were itchy, although this is quite normal for a person with Prader-Willi.

In High School, the students did not understand me either. I continued to be without friends, although I tried hard to be excepted. The students did not understand that my glands were different, I did not get hair on my face or body as they did, I was short and fat. I still have hard times dealing with the memories that haunt me today.

I wish that I had been in special education classes throughout school as I love to learn. I went through school, with so much pain and harassment at school because I wanted to learn so much.

I feel that if I had a 1-1 support person at school I would have succeeded. The hunger urges at school were difficult to control. Whenever there were holidays and special occasions I would become overwhelmed when food was around. It was hard to watch other stu-dents eat snacks. I tried to ignore the snacks the best I could, but then I became agitated and started constantly trying to sneak food, and at school and at home. I didn't mean to be a sneak, but I could not help myself. The food desire was in control!

In school I reported concerns about teachers and mistreat-ment which was true. I was sent to see a Child Psychologist for testing, as they thought I was crazy. My memories of this are like yesterday and still very painful.

My experiences with the medical profession were not successful either. For your information my father was a doctor and my mother was a nurse. They were educated parents, although little is known about Prader-Willi. My father arranged for me to see a doctor at Sun-nybrook Hospital about my condition and growth hormones. I started on hormone treatment in 1974. While at Sunnybrook I was unfortunately hypnotized and from then on I had horrible hallucinations and started hearing voices until 1986. Please do not hypnotize us.

In about 1985 – now in British Columbia – I was taken to the psychiatric ward at Shaunessy Hospital for eating disorders as my weight was way out of control. That was a nightmare! CPZ overdose, abuse and nothing to do. I was then sent to Riverview Psychiatric Hospital in order to monitor my food.

When I was at Riverview Hospital they took me off drugs. I remember the doctor there who specialized in eating disorders, trying to understand my syndrome. After 2 months my Mom brought me back home as she said I did not belong there. They realized the Prader-Willi characteristics were causing the problems with weight.

At home, my mom tried hard to control food. I could not help myself. If I was left alone I would eat everything I could. I would think about food all of the time, food is everywhere – on TV, at school, at home and in the junk mail and Internet! I would even hide food and sneak food that belonged to my brothers and sisters. I had no control. I could feel sharp teeth tearing up my stomach like piranhas, and still do. I had an overwhelming feeling with the syndrome that manifests itself as starvation – something I couldn't explain to the doctors. My mom was quite often heartbroken trying to help me control my hunger urges.

I went to stay at an adult care home to lose weight where residents were severely brain-damaged. When my weight was down to 185 pounds I was told that I really should not be there so that I was sent to a government institution for schizophrenics as to restore their place for me to go. AGAIN, I was put on CPZ. From there I was sent to an experimental Prader-Willi group home (that closed later due to a lack of funding). My weight went from 185 pounds to 225 pounds in 3 weeks. The reason for my weight gain was that I was left in the shopping mall from 7:00 a.m. Until 6:00 p.m. on my own. The group home staff said they had to take the other two clients to sheltered workshops and that I did not qualify to participate.

I came home again after the awful experience in this group home setting. I would like to let you know that the two other Prader-Willi clients have since died from excessive weight gain.

In addition to dealing with my constant weight battle, I had so many negative experiences with the staff at hospitals, residences, agencies and family members who did not understand the syndrome I live with. At that time, I didn't understand either. I had a male nurse who told me that I "would make history as the first human vacuum" to make me eat my own poo, I had a male nurse who made me clean vomit, even though people with Prader-Willi cannot vomit, I have been locked in and out of bathrooms, received stitches and broken teeth from being physically attacked by residents, had drunk workers, been placed with acutely brain damaged and psychiatric patients, been abused by staff over food and bed wetting and toiletting issues and endless, inappropriate residential placements throughout my life.

I feel that I have had a very hard life. However, now at 40 years of age I have moved to the Durham area. I know that with support and my new friends I CAN have a better life. I want to have the CHOICE to decide what I want in my life. I want to have an apartment with my own support workers to help me keep myself and my apartment clean, to monitor my food intake and keep me safe. I know that I need someone to keep the cupboards locked, and I need someone to keep me active to control my weight. I want to have some fun in my life.

I have the right to have the same CHOICES in life that you do. Without choices my right to freedom is being denied. Your child has the right to choose the <u>quality</u> of their life. You have the right to determine what the BEST choice is for your child. What will happen to us when you are gone, if there are no supports in place for us? Will we be forced to live in group homes, managed care facilities, with people we do not know or like?

As a Member at Large of People's First Ontario, we question the Government's right to impose on us "level of support" rating systems. They are ranking our needs in the similar manner of Hitler. What next? The showers and gassing? This really scares me! Who has a right to know about my personal care and hygiene needs?

This new system will invade my family's privacy. This ranking system can decide that your child does not need any workers and that you will receive no funding for support. . . .

The government believes that removing supports and not providing supports will cut the deficit, but it is really putting people in crisis situations. This is NOT cost effective or a COMMON SENSE REVOLUTION!! What is more important dollars, or people?

If the government has money to fund crisis situations, why can they not prevent situations from becoming a crisis. I need full support

NOW before I get into a crisis situation. I want to live and I am sure that you want the same for your child.

PLEASE PROTECT US from the impending doom imposed on us .... We need to act together before, it is too late!

[*John received a standing ovation from the more than 400 people present.*]

7

Conclusion

This examination of Canadians with PWS over age 40 has relied on input from those with PWS, their parents/guardians, other family members, caregivers and support workers. The multiple sources of in-put have corroborated personal information and stories, and have provided a broad perspective on PWS concerns. The interviews, mainly conducted in residences, allowed for observation of living conditions and the dynamics of relationships. The fact that 2 of those profiled had been known to the author for over 10 years, and 9 for 22 years helped provide a longitudinal perspective, a chance to see the effects of changes over time.

While the number of subjects is small, it is representative of the experiences of older Canadians with PWS. The personal stories illustrate the provision of social services in four provinces. They describe the individualization of programs and residential, vocational, recreational, and social aspects of living in community. The quality of life framework places emphasizes on concepts such as independence, choice making, relationships and opportunities for personal growth.

The individual stories illustrate the variability within Prader-Willi syndrome. They acquaint the reader with real people who face understandable struggles. All are aging, with various aches and pains, hopes, and desires. They are adults, with some very special needs. They value their independence, relationships, activities, and possessions, in the same fashion as those who provide supports and services to them.

In the routines of daily life, families lose track of papers and forget results and even purposes of tests. While this leads to incomplete documentation, it also illustrates that lifestyle is dependent on more than what medical science can provide. From a quality of life perspective, it is importance to assess the supports for preferred residential options, work or day program alternatives, and social/recreational opportunities. It is in the home, school, and community where quality of care is evident; it is in the minds of individuals where quality of life is judged.

The individuals profiled in this document, for the most part, expressed satisfaction with their quality of life. Their concerns were relatively minor when compared to some of the crises being faced by younger adults with PWS within the same provinces. Most of their parents and guardians expressed appreciation for the programs and services that were being provided, notwithstanding the anxiety and frustrations associated with economic and bureaucratic systems. The relationship with their son or daughter contributed importantly to their quality of life.

The adults with PWS profiled in the present document, and their parents and guardians, shared their personal information and stories with the understanding that they might be able to help others. They continue to be the real experts on the syndrome.

While individuals can contribute snapshot information from time to time, it is important from a research perspective for investigators to design longitudinal studies in order to observe trends over time. The early literature suggested a shortened lifespan, yet aging is now becoming a concern. Parents and professionals need to engage in this next level of dialogue. Aging with PWS will present new challenges to families, professionals and service systems in the future.

Postscript

Initial interviews for this project took place in the summer of 2007. In the more than two years until the final editing of this document, there were a number of life events which impacted the quality of lives of the thirteen individuals profiled. These included:

- death of a father
- death of a mother
- stroke of a mother
- parent cancer
- changes of guardianship
- retirement of a long-term caregiver
- resignations of support staff
- lack of available and qualified staff to hire
- loss of a day program
- conflict in residential placement
- change of personal residence
- losses of girlfriends and boyfriends
- abuse in a relationship
- loss of a pet
- emergency room visits
- hospitalization
- changes in medications
- death of a participant with PWS.

Few of these life events are uniquely associated with PWS. Some, such as the loss or incapacitation of parents, changes in guardianship, and the retirement of staff are directly related to aging. Others are concerned with economic circumstances, relationship issues, and health problems. Together they illustrate the normalcy of this "senior" stage of life.

Appendix
Prader-Willi syndrome organizations

The Foundation for Prader-Willi Research Canada

19-130825 Yonge Street Suite #370
Richmond Hill, Ontario, L4E 0K2
Event website: www.onesmallstep.ca
Information website: www.fpwr.ca

A charitable organization comprised of parents, families, researchers, and others interested in addressing issues related to Prader-Willi syndrome (PWS) and childhood obesity. Founded in 2006 by parents of children with PWS, the mission of the Foundation for Prader-Willi Research Canada (FPWRC) is to eliminate the challenges of PWS through the advancement of research. Members of FPWRC believe that through research, treatments will be found that will lessen the restrictions placed on people with PWS. These advancements will provide those with the syndrome an opportunity to lead more independent lives. All proceeds support PWS research.

In May of 2009 the FPWRC joined with the Canadian Prader-Willi Syndrome Association to become the national body representing PWS in Canada.

Canadian PWS provincial associations:

Alberta Prader-Willi Syndrome Association
c/o 9006-120 St.
Edmonton, AB, T6G 1X7
website: www.pwsa-ab.ca

British Columbia Prader-Willi Syndrome Association
c/o 2129 Lillooet Cr.
Kelowna, BC, V1V 1W3
website: www.bcpwsa.com

Ontario Prader-Willi Syndrome Association
2788 Bathurst Street, Suite 303
Toronto, Ontario, M6B 3A3
Tel: (416) 481-8657Fax: (416) 481-6706
email: opwsa@rogers.com
website: www.opwsa.com

PWS Canada E-Group

http://health.groups.yahoo.com/group/PWScanada/

An on-line group of parents, caregivers, service providers and professionals offering support to those dealing with Prader-Willi syndrome. This site offers a forum for sharing and discussing information about educational and medical issues, parenting strategies, personal stories, and connecting with other families.

Prader-Willi Syndrome Network

c/o Community Living Dufferin
29 Centennial Road, Unit #10,
Orangeville, ON L9W 1R1
email address: info@pwsnetwork.ca
website: www.pwsnetwork.ca/pws/

A network providing information and resources for service providers who work with individuals with PWS and their families. This site focusses on social service issues and not medical research or treatment.

Prader-Willi.ca

website: www.prader-willi.ca

A privately-sponsored web site that supports the quality of life of individuals with PWS and their families through the promotion of Canadian resources for non-medical aspects of PWS,

The Prader-Willi Syndrome Association (USA)

8588 Potter Park Drive, Suite 500
Sarasota, Florida 34238 USA
Tel: (800) 926-4797
Tel: (941) 312-0400
Fax: (941) 312-0142
website: www.pwsausa.org

The American organization of families and professionals working together to promote and fund research, provide education, and offer support to enhance the quality of life of those affected by Prader-Willi syndrome. Membership is available to anyone with an interest in PWS. Newsletter: *The Gathered View.*

International Prader-Willi Syndrome Organization

website: www.ipwso.org

A global organization of parents, friends, and professionals committed to enhancing the quality of life for people with PWS and their families. IPWSO has 81 member and associate member countries, representing some 25,000 families. Every three years the IPWSO sponsors an international conference, hosted by a different country, where professionals, scientists, and researchers enjoy a universal exchange of research, experience, and ideas. Newsletter: *Wavelength* (available free on-line).

References

Alexander, R.C., Van Dyke, D.C., & Hanson, J.W. (1995). Overview. In L.R. Greenswag & R.C. Alexander (Eds.), *Management of Prader-Willi Syndrome* (2nd ed.) (pp. 5-15). New York: Springer-Verlag.

Alzheimer's Disease International. (2003, February). Dementia and intellectual disabilities. Retrieved April 14, 2009, from http://www/alz.co.uk/adi/pdf/intellectualdisabilities.pdf

Balko, K. (2005). *Red yellow green system for weight management.* Toronto, ON: Ontario Prader-Willi Syndrome Association.

Boer, H., Holland, A., Whittington, J., Butler, J., Webb, T., & Clarke, D. (2002). Psychotic illness in people with Prader-Willi syndrome due to chromosome 15 maternal uniparental disomy. *Lancet, 359,* 135-136.

Brown, I., & Brown, R. I. (2003). *Quality of life and disability.* New York: Jessica Kingsley.

Butler, M.G. (2000). A 68 year old white female with Prader-Willi syndrome. *Clinical Dysmorphology, 9*(1), 65-67.

Butler, M.G., & Meaney, F.J. (1991). Standards for selected anthropometric measurements in Prader-Willi syndrome. *Pediatrics, 88*(4), 853-860.

Butler, M.G., Meaney, F.J., & Palmer, C.G. (1986). Clinical and cytogenetic survey of 39 adults with Prader-Willi syndrome. *American Journal of Medical Genetics, 23,* 793-809.

Butler, M.G., & Palmer, C.G. (1983). Parental origin of chromosome 15 deletion in Prader-Willi syndrome. *Lancet, I,* 285-286.

Canadian Association for Community Living (2008). *All about CACL.* Retrieved December 8, 2008, from http://www.cacl.ca/english/aboutus/index_asp

Carpenter, P. K. (1994). Prader-Willi syndrome in old age. *Journal of Intellectual Disability Research, 38,* 529-531.

Carrel, A.L., Lee, P.D.K., & Mozul, H.R. (2006). Growth hormone and Prader-Willi syndrome. In M.G. Butler, P.D.K. Lee, & B.Y. Whitman (Eds.), *Management of Prader-Willi syndrome* (3rd ed.) (pp. 201-241). New York: Springer.

Carter, T.O. (1991, September 9). An appetite for freedom. *British Columbia Report, 3*(2), 31.

Cassidy, S.B. (1984). Prader-Willi syndrome. *Current Problems in Pediatrics, XIV*(1).

Cassidy, S.B., Devi, A., & Mukaida, R.D. (1995, June). Aging in Prader- Willi syndrome. 2nd Prader-Willi Syndrome International Scientific Workshop and Conference Abstract Book (Abstract 27), Somarka, Oslo.

Cassidy, S.B., & Schwartz, S. (2009, September). Prader-Willi syndrome. In: GeneReviews at GeneTests: Medical Genetics Information Resource (database online). Copyright, University of Washington, Seattle. 1997-2008. Retrieved January 07, 2010, from http://www.genetests.org

Christensen, C.S., & Hainline, B.E. (2001, September/October). PWS and obesity, and PWS look-alikes. *The Gathered View, 26*(5), 4-5.

Clarke, D.J., Boer, H., Chung, M.C., Sturney, P., & Webb, T. (1996). Maladaptive behaviour in Prader-Willi syndrome. *Intellectual Disability Research, 40*(Pt. 2), 159-165.

Clarke, D.J., Boer, H., Whittington, J., Holland, A., Butler, J., & Webb, T. (2002). Prader-Willi syndrome, compulsive and ritualistic behaviours: The first population-based survey. *The British Journal of Psychiatry, 180*, 358-362.

Community Living Research Project. (2006). *Services for seniors with a developmental disability: Literature and initial program review*. Vancouver, BC: UBC School of Social Work and Family Studies.

Community Living Research Project. (2008). *Residential alternatives in B.C.* Vancouver, BC: UBC School of Social Work.

Cryderman, K. (2008, March 12). Sister fears for future as home care falls short. *Calgary Herald*.

Dudley, O., McManus, B., Vogels, A., Whittington, J., & Muscatelli, F. (2008). Cross-cultural comparisons of obesity and growth in Prader-Willi syndrome. *Journal of Intellectual Disability Research, 52*(5), 426-436.

Dykens, E.M. (2002). Are jigsaw puzzle skills 'spared' in people with Prader-Willi syndrome? *Journal of Child Psychology and Psychiatry, 43,* 343-52.

Dykens, E.M. (2004). Maladaptive and compulsive behavior in Prader-Willi syndrome: New insights from older adults. *American Journal of Mental Retardation, 109*(2), 142-53.

Dyken, E.M., Cassidy, S.B. & King, B.H. (1999). Maladaptive behavior differences in Prader-Willi syndrome due to paternal deletion versus maternal uniparental disomy. *American Journal on Mental Retardation, 104,* 67-77.

Eiholzer, U., & Lee, P.D.K. (2006). Medical considerations in Prader-Willi syndrome. In M.G. Butler, P.D.K. Lee, & B.Y. Whitman (Eds.), *Management of Prader-Willi syndrome* (3rd ed.) (pp. 97-152). New York: Springer.

Einfeld, S.L., Kavanagh, S.J., Smith, A., Evans, E.J., Tonge, B.J., & Taffe, J. (2006). Mortality in Prader-Willi syndrome. *American Journal on Mental Retardation, 111*(3), 193-198.

Goldman, J.J. (1988). Prader-Willi syndrome in two institutionalized older adults. *Mental Retardation, 26*(2), 97-102.

Government of Canada. (1984). Canadian charter of rights and freedoms. Retrieved March 15, 2009, from http://www.efc.ca/pages/law/charter/charter.text.html

Greenswag, L. R. (1987). Adults with Prader-Willi syndrome: A survey of 232 cases. *Developmental Medicine and Child Neurology, 29,* 145-152.

Greenswag, L.R. (1988). Understanding psychosexuality. In L. R. Greenswag, & R. C. Alexander (Eds.) *Management of Prader-Willi Syndrome* (2nd ed.) (pp. 171-181). New York: Springer-Verlag.

Grugni G., Crino, A., Bosio, L., Corrias, A., Cuttini, M., DeToni, T., DiBattista, E., Franzese, A., et al. (2008). The Italian national survey for Prader-Willi syndrome: An epidemiologic study. *American Journal of Medical Genetics, Part A, 146*(7), 861-72.

Gunay-Aygun, M., Schwartz, S., Heeger, S., O'Riordan, M.A., & Cassidy, S.B. (2001). The changing purpose of Prader-Willi syndrome clinical diagnostic criteria and proposed revised criteria. Pediatrics, 108(5), e92. Retrieved October 18, 2008, from http://www.pediatrics.org/cgi/content/1/108/5/e92

Hanchett, J.M., & Meier, B. (1995). A crisis intervention model for persons with Prader-Willi syndrome. In L.R. Greenswag & R.C. Alexander (Eds.), *Management of Prader-Willi Syndrome* (2nd ed.) (pp. 265-273). New York: Springer-Verlag.

Harty, J.R., Hollowell, J.G., & Sieg, K.G. (1993). Tall stature: An atypical phenotype in Prader-willi syndrome. *Clinical Pediatrics,* 179-180.

Heinemann, J. (2008, March 15). Medical crisis prevention and intervention. Presentation given at the British Columbia Prader-Willi Syndrome Association Spring Conference, Vancouver, BC.

Holm, V.A., Cassidy, S.B., Butler, M.G., Hanchett, J.M., Greenswag, L.R., Whitman, B.Y., & Greenberg, F. (1993). Prader-Willi syndrome: Consensus diagnostic criteria. *Pediatrics, 91,* 398-402.

Horvath , B. (2006, October). Prader-Willi syndrome survey of Central West Region Service Providers. Toronto, ON: PWS Network Steering Committee.

IPWSO. (n.d.). A medical reference guide for parents and caregivers. Retrieved October 12, 2008, from www.ipwso.org

James, T.N. (1987). *Social and psychological aspects of Prader-Willi syndrome.* Unpublished doctoral dissertation, University of Calgary.

James, T.N. (in press). *Prader-Willi syndrome: Quality of life.* Courtenay, BC: Poplar Publilshing.

James, T.N., & Brown, R.I. (1992). *Prader-Willi syndrome: Home, school and community.* London, UK: Chapman & Hall.

Jamin, T. (1990, May). Ray Ronald (1937-1990). *Under Prairie Skies, 49,* 2.

Keuder, L. (2005). The genetics of Prader-Willi syndrome: An explanation for the rest of us. *The Gathered View, 30*(1), 8-10.

Kinash, S. (2007). *A recipe for success.* Charlotte, NC: Information Age Publishing.

Kozma, C. (2008, January/March). Aging with a developmental disability. *Topics in Geriatric Rehabilitation, 24*(1), 41-53.

Leconte, J.M. (1981). Social work intervention strategies for families with children with Prader-Willi syndrome. In V.A. Holm, S.J. Sulzbacher, & P. Pipes (Eds.), *Prader-Willi syndrome* (pp. 245-257). Baltimore: University Park Press.

Ledbetter, D.H., Riccardi, V.M., Airhart, S.D., Strobel, R.J., Keenan, B.S., & Crawford, J.D. (1981). Deletion of chromosome 15 as a cause of Prader-Willi syndrome. *New England Journal of Medicine, 304*, 325-329.

Levine, K., & Wharton, R.H. (1993). *Children with Prader-Willi syndrome: Information for school staff.* New York: Visible Ink.

Mitchell, W. (1988). Social skills training. In L.R. Greenswag & R.C. Alexander (Eds.), Management of Prader-Willi syndrome (pp. 165-170). New York: Springer-Verlag.

National Advisory Council on Aging (NACA). (2004). *Seniors on the margins: Aging with a developmental disability.* Ottawa: Author. Retrieved October 4, 2008, from http://dsp-psd.pwg sc.gc.ca/Collection/H88-5-2-2004E.pdf

Nicholls, R.D., Knoll, J.H., Butler, M.G., Karam, S., & Lalande, M. (1989). Genetic imprinting suggested by maternal hetero-disomy in nondeletion Prader-Willi syndrome. *Nature, 342*, 281-285.

Nugent, J. (2007). *Successfully supporting people with Prader-Willi syndrome: A handbook for professionals.* Toronto, ON: Prader-Willi Syndrome Network.

Okereke, O.L., Kang, J.H., Cook, N.R., Graziano, J.M., Manson, J.E., Buring, J.E., & Grodstein, F. (2008). Type 2 diabetes mellitus and cognitive decline in two large cohorts of community-dwelling older adults. *Journal of the American Geriatrics Society, 56* (6), 1028-1036.

Ontario Partnership on Aging and Developmental Disabilities. (2007a). The dynamic of denial. Retrieved April 10, 2009, from http://www.opadd.on.ca/Caregiver/dynamicofdenial.htm

Ontario Partnership on Aging and Developmental Disabilities. (2007b). Aging issues. Retrieved April 10, 2009, from http://www.opadd.on.ca/Caregiver/agingissues.htm

Ontario Partnership on Aging and Developmental Disabilities. (2007c). Transition planning. Retrieved April 10, 2009, from http://www.opadd.on.ca/Caregiver/transitionplanning.htm

Persons with Developmental Disabilities. (2008, March/April). Kip shows the way. Calgary: PDD Central Region Community Board. Retrieved April 14, 2008, from http://www.pdd.org/docs/cent/MarApr2009Newsletter.pdf

Prader, A., Labhart, A., & Willi, H. (1956). A syndrome character-
    ized by obesity, small stature, cryptorchidism, and oligophrenia,
    following a myotonia-like status in infancy. In M.G. Butler,
    P.D.K. Lee, & B.Y. Whitman (Eds.), *Management of Prader-
    Willi syndrome* (3rd ed.) (pp.467-471). New York: Springer.

Province of B.C. (2008, July 18). Community Living Authority Act
    Regulation (B.C. Reg. 228/2008, s.2.1). Retrieved May 12,
    2010, from http://www.canlii.org

PWSA-USA. (2008). Diagnostic criteria for Prader-Willi syndrome.
    Retrieved October 7, 2008, from http://www.pwsausa.org/
    syndrome/Diagnos.htm

PWS Network. (2008, January). Central east region service providers
    Prader-Willi syndrome survey May-November 2007: Final
    report. Retrieved March 15, 2009, from http://www.
    pwsnetwork.ca/pws/docs/central_east_survey_report.pdf

Roof, E., Stone, W., MacLean, W., Feurer, I.D., Thompson, T., &
    Butler, M.G. (2000). Intellectual characteristics of Prader-
    Willi syndrome: Comparison of genetic subtypes. *Journal
    of Intellectual Disability Research, 44*(Pt. 1), 25-30.

Scheimann, A.O., Lee, P.D.K., & Ellis, K.J. (2006). Gasrtointestinal
    system, obesity, and body composition. In M.G. Butler,
    P.D.K. Lee, & B.Y. Whitman (Eds.), *Management of Prader-
    Willi syndrome* (3rd ed.) (pp. 153-200). New York: Springer.

Smith, A. (1999). The diagnosis of Prader-Willi syndrome. *Journal
    of Pediatrics and Child Health, 35*, 335-337.

Special Olympics, Inc. (2005). Changing attitudes changing the
    world: The health and health care of people with intellectual
    disabilities. Retrieved October 3, 2008, from http://www.
    specialolympics.org/uploadedFiles/LandingPage/WhatWe
    Do/Research_Studies_Description_Pages/policy_paper_
    Health.pdf

Stadler, D.D. (1995). Nutritional management. In L.R. Greenswag
    & R.C. Alexander (Eds.), *Management of Prader-Willi
    Syndrome* (2nd ed.) (pp. 88-114). New York: Springer-Verlag.

Statistics Canada. (2007). Health adjusted life expectancy, by sex.
    Retrieved October 12, 2008, from http://www40.statcan.
    ca/cst01/hlth67.htm

Thomson, A.K., Glasson, E.J., & Bittles, A.H. (2006). A long-term
    population-based clinical and morbidity review of Prader-
    Willi syndrome in western Australia. *Journal of Intellectual
    Disability Research, 50*(Part 1), 69-78.

Vogels, A., DenEnde, J., Keymolen, K., Mortier, G., Devriendt, K., Leguis, E., & Fryns, J.P. (2004). Minimum prevalence, birth incidence and causes of death for Prader-Willi syndrome in Flanders. *European Journal of Human Genetics, 12,* 238-240.

Waters, J., Jewson, N., Quinn, M., & Sharma, N. (2007). *Adults with Prader-willi syndrome and their parents/carers: Report of a survey of members of PWSA(UK).* London: PWSA(UK).

Whitman, B.Y., & Greenswag, L.R. (1995). Psychological and behavioral management. In L.R. Greenswag & R.C. Alexander (Eds.), *Management of Prader-Willi Syndrome* (2nd ed.) (pp. 125-141). New York: Springer-Verlag.

Whitmer, R.A., Gustafson, D.R., Barrett-Connor, E., Haan, M.N., Gunderson, E.P., & Yaffe, K. (2008). Central obesity and increased risk of dementia more than three decades later. *Neurology, 71,* 1057-1064. Retrieved April 14, 2009, from http://www.neurology.org/cgi/content/abstract/71/14/1057

Whittington, J.E., Holland, A.J., Webb, T., Butler, J.V., Clarke, D.J., & Boer, H. (2001). Population prevalence and estimated birth incidence and mortality rate for people with Prader-Willi syndrome in one UK Health Region. *Journal of Medical Genetics, 38,* 792-798.

Whittington, J., Holland, A., Webb, T., Butler, J., Clarke, D., & Boer, H. (2004). Cognitive abilities and genotype in a population-based sample of people with Prader-Willi syndrome. *Journal of Intellectual Disability Research, 48* (Part 2), 172-187.

World Health Organization. (2006). BMI classification. Retrieved December 4, 2008, from http://www.who.int/bmi/index.jsp?introPage=intro3.html

Zellweger, H. (1981). Diagnosis and therapy in the first phase of Prader-Willi syndrome. In V.A. Holm, S. Sulzbacher, & P. Pipes (Eds.), *The Prader-Willi Syndrome* (pp. 55-68). Baltimore: University Park Press.

Subject Index

Printed in Great Britain
by Amazon

41395822R00076